Tanks and Other Tracked Vehicles
in Service

Mechanized Warfare in Colour

TANKS

and other Tracked Vehicles
in Service

by
B. T. WHITE

illustrated by
JOHN W. WOOD
B. Hiley
J. Pelling
E. Bruce

BLANDFORD PRESS
POOLE   DORSET

Blandford Press Ltd
Link House, West Street,
Poole, Dorset BH15 1LL

First published 1978
© Blandford Press 1978

Colour printed by W. S. Cowell, Ipswich
Text printed and books bound in Great Britain by
Richard Clay (The Chaucer Press), Ltd.,
Bungay, Suffolk

0 7137 0851 4

PREFACE

A selection of the more important or interesting military tracked vehicles in service today (or shortly to enter service) is included in this book. The choice is entirely the author's and has to some extent been dictated by the availability of information and suitable illustrations: the inclusion of one vehicle or omission of another should in no way be taken as an index of their relative importance.

The arrangement is broadly by country of design of the basic vehicle, but where a modification is carried out in a different country to that of design so as to radically modify the original function or design, the second country is given credit in the page heading. Also, where a country is the major producer of a vehicle designed elsewhere, this may likewise be noted in the title. It should be mentioned here that Italy, for example, is a major producer of German and American equipment but not in greater numbers than in the countries of its origin.

Under each country, the general arrangement is under main battle tanks, light tanks, armoured personnel carriers, self-propelled guns, missile carriers and support vehicles. However, this strict arrangement cannot always be followed where, for wider coverage, two different types of vehicle are included in one plate.

Vehicles are shown in typical colours for the country represented. In order to emphasize the widespread export of fighting vehicles by some of the major countries, as well as to add interest to the illustrations, some user countries as well as those of design are included.

Camouflage colours are liable to be changed without notice, but some notes on schemes in use in different countries are included in an Appendix at the end of the book.

A few cross-sectional drawings of modern tracked fighting vehicles are also included to supplement the coloured views by giving a general idea of interiors. These section views cannot, however, necessarily be taken as being either fully up to date or complete in detail. Many modern fighting vehicles, which are very costly machines, are progressively up-dated during their time in service. Illustrations which are released for publication will have classified details omitted.

Tabulated data on the majority of vehicles in the book is included in a further Appendix. This should be taken as a rough comparative guide only. Methods of assessing performance vary between different countries, for example, and data on the vehicles of some countries cannot be guaranteed.

The information drawn on in preparing this book has come from many sources, varying from manufacturers, or military attachés to the author's friends, among whom in particular must be mentioned Colonel Robert J. Icks, who has an unrivalled collection on the subject of A.F.V.s. For published sources, however, the author would particularly like to mention the works of Richard M. Ogorkiewicz, the outstanding writer on A.F.V. design, and Christopher F. Foss, who is one of the leading writers in English on the development of current military vehicles. No one interested in the history and development of A.F.V.s should overlook the two excellent journals *A.F.V. News* (published in Ontario, Canada) and *Tankette* (published in England). The author gratefully acknowledges the help he has received from all sources.

If this book has aroused in the reader an interest for the first time in armoured fighting vehicles, he is recommended to visit some of the tank museums which now are established in many different countries, of which the Royal Armoured Corps Tank Museum at Bovington, Dorset, England is one of the earliest and certainly one of the best.

B. T. WHITE
London, 1977

INTRODUCTION

The object of this Introduction is to draw attention to some of the problems encountered in the design of a modern armoured fighting vehicle—which is always a compromise between protection, mobility and armament—and the answers arrived at by different countries. Solutions to these problems have been influenced by differing tactical and operational criteria and—even for the richest countries—cost.

Tracks versus wheels

Only tracked fighting vehicles are covered in this book. Effectively, this category includes all main battle tanks today, nearly all self-propelled guns and heavy support vehicles, such as bridge-layers, all of which require a stable platform.

The lighter categories of armoured vehicle, such as for reconnaissance or personnel carrying, are by no means confined to tracks, however. The greater simplicity, cheapness, speed, reliability and lower noise factor of wheeled vehicles all have their attractions where size and stability allow wheels instead of tracks to be used and where a generally lower cross-country performance is acceptable.

Main Battle Tanks

Now that the practicable maximum size of a tank gun seems to have been reached and is tending to become almost standard (at around 120 mm. for rifled guns) so that the old categories of

medium and heavy tank have become merged, the self-explanatory term 'main battle tank' has become popular.

The layout of a centrally mounted turret containing a gun of between 100 mm. and 125 mm. on a hull with the engine mounted at the rear is almost universal, although preferences for drive to sprockets at the front of the track (an easier distribution of weight and components but at the penalty of a transmission shaft running through the floor of the fighting compartment) or rear of the track vary.

Guns

Guns, within the range of calibres mentioned, vary from conventional rifled construction to smooth bore weapons firing fin-stabilized projectiles. In between is the French method of a rifled gun firing a projectile in which the warhead inside has its rotation retarded. Automatic loading is not yet common but is likely to be more so, since heavy rounds of around 120-mm. calibre are difficult to handle manually unless, as in the British Chieftain, the charge and projectile are loaded separately: a system likely to slow down the rate of fire. Range-finders vary from optical to laser, with future development tending to concentrate on the latter. The use of a heavy machine-gun for ranging the main gun avoids the need for ballistic corrections (manually or by computer) but can be slower in operation and cannot be used up to the full range of the gun. Complete or partial stabilization of the gun is now almost universal. This enables the gun to be fired while the vehicle is moving, although aiming on the move, with a stop for final sighting adjustments before firing, would be more normal.

All main battle tanks carry a machine-gun mounted coaxially with the main gun and most also have another machine-gun on the turret roof, sometimes capable of being controlled from inside the tank. This is usually described as an anti-aircraft weapon, although it is also available for area defence. Practice varies between countries as to whether the tank commander has the task of being a part-time machine-gunner, or another member of the turret crew, usually the loader. Machine-guns in the front glacis plate, once so common, have lost favour because, apart from being only rarely useful, they reduce somewhat the effectiveness of the frontal armour and take up valuable stowage space.

Night vision devices, such as infra-red searchlights are fitted to, or available for, most modern battle tanks and other A.F.V.s.

A means of making smoke for self-protection is present in all main battle tanks. In Soviet tanks this is done by vaporized diesel fuel being injected into the exhaust system, but elsewhere multiple dischargers for smoke grenades are more usual. These are generally mounted on the turret.

Protection
This tends to vary in accordance with the relative importance attached to armour as opposed to mobility. Actual figures, for current main battle tanks,

are rarely published but the thickest armour continues to be concentrated on frontal surfaces of hull and turret. Steel armour is still used for most M.B.T.s, although laminated armour, such as the British 'Chobham Armour', which is claimed to give good protection against all types of projectiles from solid shot to hollow charge, may become widespread. Protection of another kind—against nuclear fallout, biological or chemical (N.B.C.) warfare is provided for in most modern main battle tanks. This usually consists of a means of maintaining the air pressure inside the vehicle at a slightly higher level than outside, preventing the entry of toxic matter.

Keeping the size of a tank (and particularly its height) down as far as possible, and so decreasing the size of the target it presents is a form of passive protection. A low turret is desirable, but this can have disadvantages—as in Soviet tanks—of limiting gun depression. Eliminating the turret altogether—as in the Swedish S-tank— is one solution, as is the use of variable suspension height. The Japanese have taken advantage of the fact that the average Japanese soldier is smaller than his Western counterpart and scaled down the size of their tanks accordingly.

Engines
Diesel engines (or multi-fuel engines, which are usually modified diesels) are now used in nearly all modern main battle tanks. At least 700 h.p. for a tank of around 50 tons is regarded as necessary to provide an acceptable

power : weight ratio and the mobility which largely depends on it. The dual system, where a diesel engine is combined with a gas turbine—the diesel for normal economic running and the turbine for giving extra power when needed—has worked well in the Swedish S-tank but has not been copied elsewhere, although a gas turbine has now been adopted for the latest American battle tank, the XM-I.

Transmission systems are still manual or semi-manual in some cases, but automatic transmissions are also used. Steering systems often are linked with the transmission, so that turns of varying radii are associated with different gear ratios. There are many varieties of steering for tracked vehicles, ranging from the relatively simple clutch and brake type upwards and for a lucid discussion of these (and, indeed, all aspects of fighting vehicle design) the reader is recommended to refer to *Design and Development of Fighting Vehicles*, R. M. Ogorkiewicz, London, 1968.

Suspension

The most common system today is where each road-wheel is independently sprung on a torsion bar, which passes transversely under the belly of the tank. The main disadvantage of this well-tried and efficient system is that it takes up space inside the armour of the vehicle and/or tends to increase its height—an important feature in a tank. The Horstmann type—road-wheels, sprung in pairs, the two wheels on the bogey being controlled by horizontal springs—used on the British Centurion

and Chieftain is also reliable but probably does not equal the riding qualities of the better independent systems. It leaves the interior of the hull clear, however, as does the Belleville washer system used on Swiss battle tanks. Hydropneumatic suspension systems give a good ride, but may be less reliable and require more maintenance than simpler types.

Tracks are usually of cast steel and the use of rubber pads on the shoes to cut down damage to roads, as well as wear on the tracks themselves on hard surfaces, is now common in the tanks of most countries except those in the Soviet bloc.

Mobility

The German Leopard, with a maximum road speed of 65 km./hr is one of the fastest modern main battle tanks, while the British Chieftain at 48 km./hr is one of the slowest. It is claimed, however, that the cross-country performance of a tank is more important than high road speed and the latter does not necessarily mean that a tank is proportionately fast off roads, where performance will vary widely according to the type of terrain but, in any case, may well be limited by the endurance of the tank crew. It is impossible to quote comparable cross-country speeds, but types of tracks and their ground-bearing area; the ground pressure of the vehicle and the type of suspension are all-important factors.

The comparatively light 38-ton Vickers Main Battle Tank is fully amphibious with the use of nylon screens to increase its buoyancy: it is

9

propelled by its tracks in water. Other, heavier, battle tanks, in the absence of bridges, can usually negotiate water obstacles only by deep wading, with the vehicle fully sealed and using breathing tubes for the air supply, such as that shown for the French AMX30 in this book.

Light Tanks

Vehicles that can loosely be classified as light tanks may vary widely in the function for which they are used in different countries. The French AMX 13 and Austrian Kürassier, for example, are tank destroyers, whereas the Swedish Ikv-91 is classified as an 'Infantry Gun Vehicle'. Generally, however, the role of light tanks is for fighting reconnaissance or to be air-droppable (or at least capable of being carried by air) in support of airborne formations. Their armament can be as powerful as that of a main battle tank (such as the U.S. M-551's 152-mm. gun-launcher) but the ammunition supply and protection is usually very much less. The top speed is usually higher than that of most main battle tanks (U.S. M-551—70 km./hr, British Scorpion—81 km./hr) although, depending on size and other factors, the cross-country speed may in some cases be lower. Water mobility is nearly always provided for, either without preparation (except usually the raising of a surf board or trim vane and starting a bilge pump) or by the use of flotation screens carried as standard and capable of being erected in a few minutes. Propulsion in water is, nowadays, usually either by means of hydro-jets

or the vehicle's tracks. Soviet practice tends to favour amphibious tanks (such as PT-76) propelled by water jets, while Britain and the U.S.A. prefer smaller, more compact reconnaissance tanks which therefore have less inherent buoyancy and need aids to float. Tanks propelled by their tracks when afloat cannot attain the same water speeds as hydro jet-propelled vehicles.

The armament of light tanks may, in some cases, be augmented by anti-tank missile launchers to supplement the conventional gun, which may lack range and power for defence against heavier armour.

Light alloy metal construction is becoming increasingly used for light tanks, whose general layout may often correspond to that of main battle tanks, although in the British Scorpion, for example, a front location for the engine has been adopted. Although not necessarily a prime consideration, a front engine location enhances crew protection.

Armoured Personnel Carriers

These are in two categories today:

Armoured Personnel Carriers (as evolved from features of vehicles like the British Universal Carrier, the German armoured half-tracked infantry carriers and converted tanks of World War II); and Mechanized Infantry Combat Vehicles, from which infantry can fight without dismounting. The latter generally have a turret-mounted weapon of 20-mm. calibre upwards, which may be supplemented by anti-tank missile launchers, and are fully provided with ports from which the infantry carried can operate their personal weapons. The M.I.C.V. has evolved from the normal A.P.C., however, and distinction between the two types is not always clear-cut.

The American M-113 pioneered the use of light alloy construction in light armoured vehicles and this is becoming common for many A.P.C.s/M.I.C.V.s today.

The majority of armoured personnel carriers can swim without special preparation, but the development of the Landing Vehicle Tracked category of personnel/load carrier, capable of operation in the open sea, has continued mainly in the United States.

The internal layout of A.P.C.s varies between different countries, but location of the engine at the front of the vehicle, leaving an unobstructed compartment at the rear (with doors in the hull rear plate) for the infantry carried, is a very common feature. Size and protection can vary widely, from the German Marder of 28 tons for instance, carrying a total of ten men and able to accompany main battle tanks, to the French AMX10 P, half the Marder's weight but carrying eleven men.

In most countries, A.P.C.s/M.I.C.V.s are used as the basis for specialized variants, such as mortar carriers, command vehicles, etc.

Self-Propelled Guns
Today, these fall into three broad categories:

Anti-tank; Field; Anti-Aircraft; although most S.P. guns carry a range of ammunition to enable them to carry out alternative functions.

The chassis used are adapted from those of battle tanks, light tanks or armoured personnel carriers in most cases or, at least, have many features in common with them. Some anti-aircraft tanks, such as the German Gepard, based on the Leopard, or the French twin 30 mm. mounting on the AMX 30 chassis, have layouts closest to their parent vehicles. Self-propelled anti-tank guns, like the German Jagdpanzerkanone and the Soviet ASU-85 mostly trace their ancestry to the assault guns of World War II—low, well-armoured vehicles with weapons having a limited traverse, although the anti-tank guided missile vehicles which are tending to replace them, being able to fire from off line or concealed positions, are not subject to the same design considerations. The German Jagdpanzer Rakete, adapted from the Jagdpanzerkanone, may be contrasted with the lightly armoured British Striker, which is similar to the Spartan armoured personnel carrier.

Self-propelled field artillery, with weapons from 105 mm. up to medium calibres (the U.S. 175-mm. gun or 203-mm. howitzer, for example) as a class tends to use more specialized chassis. Although these may use engines and elements of suspension in common with other vehicles, a front engine layout, leaving the back end clear for the gun and easy access for its service, is almost universal. Except for the 105-mm. British Abbot, a calibre of 155 mm. is generally regarded as the minimum for field pieces. Apart from some vehicles required to be air portable, where weight has to be reduced, most modern guns are in revolving turrets which give the crew protection at least against small arms ammunition and shell splinters and can be sealed against N.B.C. attack. Automatic or semi-automatic loading is becoming common on heavier weapons for field or anti-tank use. On the American M–109, for instance, it can double the rate of fire.

Anti-aircraft self-propelled guns (or anti-aircraft tanks as some are categorized) vary in capability from fire over open sights only to all weather day or night operation, controlled by radar and computer. All tend nowadays, however, to be multiple mountings of automatic guns limited to calibres of up to 35 mm. for use against close low-level attack only. Guided weapons are more generally being used for medium to long-range air defence. Some or all of the associated radar equipment is carried in accompanying vehicles.

Missile Carriers

The Soviet Union is tending to turn to high-mobility wheeled vehicles as carriers and launchers for its medium to long-range surface to surface missiles. The United States, on the other hand, has moved from the truck-mounted Honest John tactical missile system to the Lance, which has a tracked carrier-launcher. The French Pluton system has been designed from the start to be carried on tracked vehicles, of the AMX 30 type, so there is no general consensus of thought on the type of mobility to be given to such weapons.

Support Vehicles

In most countries, there is a desire to achieve as high as possible a degree of commonality of chassis between support vehicles (such as for recovery, bridging and engineer tasks) and the main battle tanks or other vehicles with which they are to work. The advantages of having the same level of battlefield mobility, common mechanical spares etc. need no emphasis. Most countries have support vehicles in the main categories using the same chassis as their current main battle tank, only the Soviet Union apparently continuing to make wide use of the chassis of obsolescent tanks.

Armoured Recovery Vehicles are all equipped with a winch and towing gear and some, such as the German Leopard and French AMX 30D, have revolving cranes for such tasks as engine changes. Some countries, such as Sweden, base their main recovery vehicle on a lighter type of chassis, leaving actual battlefield recovery of main battle tanks to other tanks. Most countries also have light recovery vehicles capable of dealing with armoured vehicles of their own class, such as armoured personnel carriers, light tanks and some self-propelled guns.

Most tank bridge layers, or armoured vehicle launched bridges (A.V.L.B.), continue to carry either a rigid single span bridge or a folded bridge of the 'Scissors' type. The latter, because of its more compact travelling configuration, is the more popular although its height during the laying process makes it more conspicuous in the battle area. The German Biber on the Leopard chassis, by using a span in two halves sliding forward for launching, combines advantages of both the earlier types. The most common means of launching is hydraulic, with power take-off from the main engine of the vehicle.

Pioneer vehicles, for battlefield tasks such as the demolition of obstacles and preparation of gun positions etc. are either standard tanks with attachments, such as dozer blades, or adaptations of main battle-tank chassis. In some countries, such as France, the armoured recovery vehicle (AMX 30D) can also act as a pioneer vehicle, or the pioneer vehicle is very similar to the recovery vehicle, as in West Germany. Only in the United Kingdom has a completely new vehicle, the Combat Engineer Tractor, which is unlike any existing chassis, been produced for the pioneer role. Many of the World War II devices for minefield clearance, such as rollers, ploughs and explosive devices, are represented in various armies today. The United Kingdom, for example, has a rocket-propelled explosive device (carried in a trailer towed by the Combat Engineer Tractor) while the Warsaw Pact countries have an array of roller and plough devices for attachment to main battle tanks. Mines can be laid mechanically by devices towed or carried by such vehicles as the British FV 432 armoured personnel carrier.

Command, signal, radar and ambulance functions are carried out, in most countries today, by adaptations of armoured personnel carrier chassis.

THE COLOURED ILLUSTRATIONS

A description of each coloured
plate is given between pages
81 and 138

1 Tanque Argentino Mediano (TAM)

2 Carrier, Full
Tracked,
Armoured,
M-113A1,
Fire Support
Vehicle, with
Saladin turret
(*above*) and
Scorpion
turret

3 Panzerjäger Kürassier

4 Schützenpanzer 4K4FA-G (*above*) and Schützenpanzer 4K4FA

5   Type T-59 Main Battle Tank (*above*) and Type K-63
    Armoured Personnel Carrier

Czechoslovakia

6 Obrneny Transporter – OT.62 (TOPAS)

7 Char de Combat AMX 30

8 Char de 13t
à Canon de
105-mm.
(Char Léger
AMX 13)
(*above*) and
Bitube de
30-mm.
Anti-Aérien
Automoteur
(AMX 13)

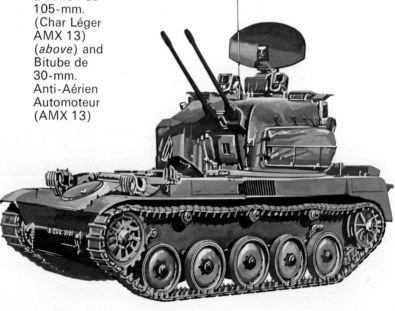

9 Véhicule de Combat d'Infanterie AMX 10P (*above*) and Véhicule de Combat d'Infanterie AMX 13

10 Canon Automoteur de 155-mm. GCT (*above*) and Obusier Automouvant de 155-mm. AMX 13

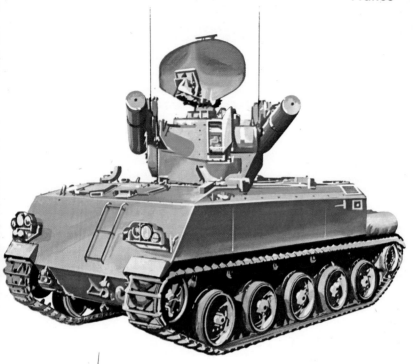

11 Véhicule de Tir Roland AMX 30
(*above*) and Véhicule de Tir Pluton
AMX 30

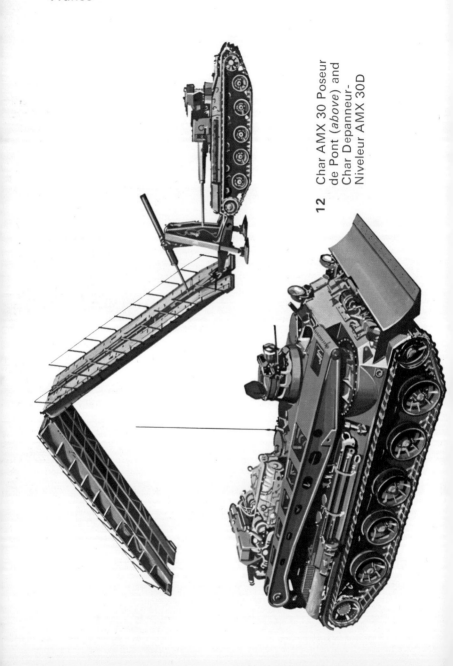

12 Char AMX 30 Poseur de Pont (*above*) and Char Depanneur-Niveleur AMX 30D

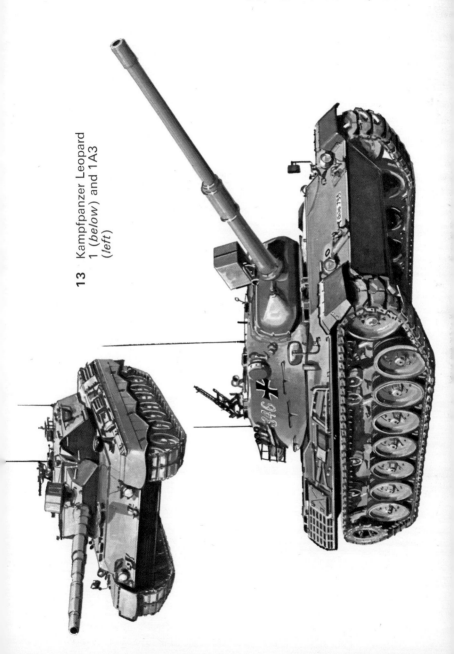

13 Kampfpanzer Leopard 1 (*below*) and 1A3 (*left*)

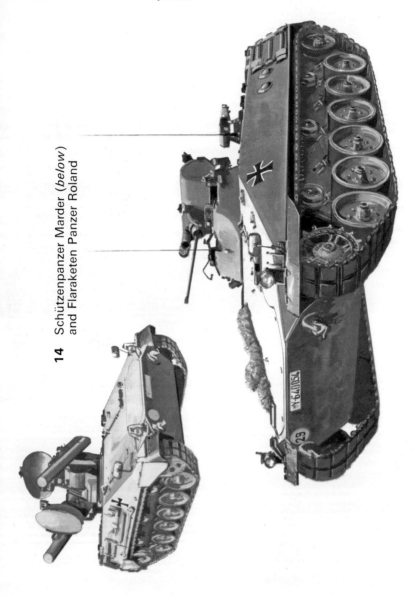

14 Schützenpanzer Marder (*below*) and Flaraketen Panzer Roland

German Federal Republic/Holland

15 Flakpanzer 1 Gepard (*below*) and Pantserrups LUA 35-mm.

16 Kanonenjagdpanzer KJPZ4-5 (*above*) and
Raketenjagdpanzer RJPZ3

17 Bergepanzer 2 Leopard (*below*) and Brückenlegepanzer 1 Biber

18 Self-Propelled 160-mm. Mortar (*below*) and Self-propelled 155-mm. Gun-Howitzer

19 Tank, Type 74, 105-mm. Gun (*above*) and Tank, Type 61, 90-mm. Gun

20 Armoured Personnel Carrier, Type 73 (*above*) and
Armoured Personnel Carrier, Type 60

21 Self-Propelled 106-mm. Recoilless Gun, Type 60
    (*above*) and 4.2 inch Mortar Carriage, Type 60

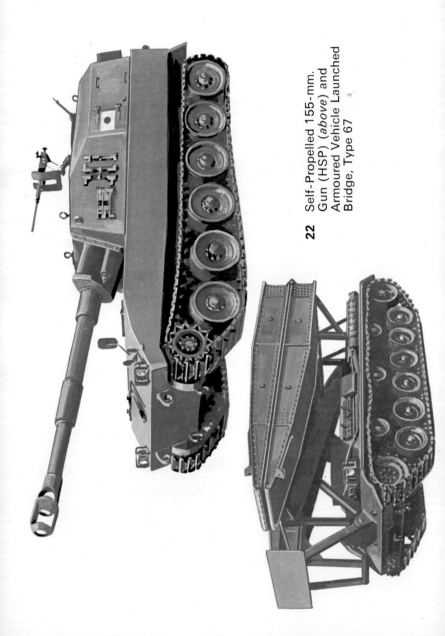

22 Self-Propelled 155-mm.
Gun (HSP) (*above*) and
Armoured Vehicle Launched
Bridge, Type 67

23 T-72 (Main Battle Tank)

24 T-62 (Main Battle Tank)

Soviet Union

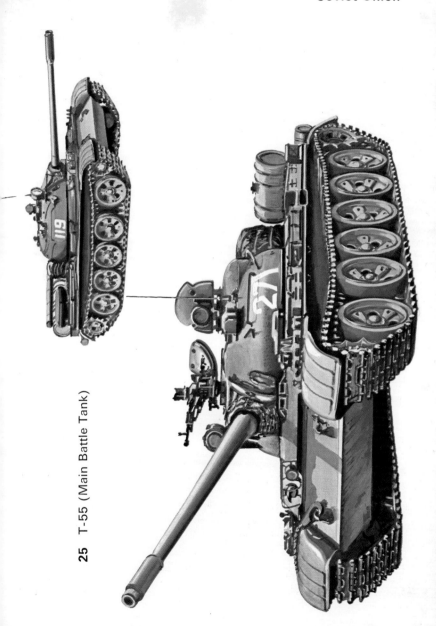

25 T-55 (Main Battle Tank)

26 ASU-85 (Airborne Assault Gun) (*above*) and PT-76 (Amphibious Tank)

27 BMP-1 (Infantry Combat Vehicle) (*above*) and BMD (Airborne Combat Vehicle)

28 ZSU-23-4 (Anti-Aircraft
S.P. Gun) (*above*) and
ZSU-57-2 (Anti-Aircraft
S.P. Gun)

29 SU-122 (Self-Propelled Gun)

30 SA.6 Gainful (Anti-Aircraft Missile Carrier) (*below*) and Straight Flush (Armoured Fire Control Vehicle)

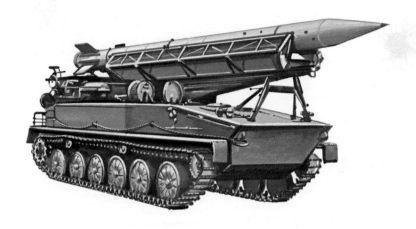

31 Frog 5 (Missile Carrier) (*above*) and SA-4 Ganef (Anti-Aircraft Missile Carrier)

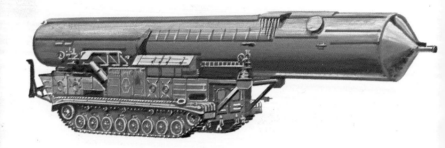

32 SS-15 (Scrooge) (Strategic Missile Carrier) (*above*)
and SS-14 Scamp (Scapegoat)

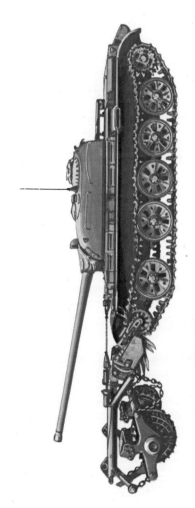

33 T-54/MTU (Tank Bridgelayer) (*above*) and T-54/PT (Tank Mineclearer)

34 Stridsvagn Strv. 103B

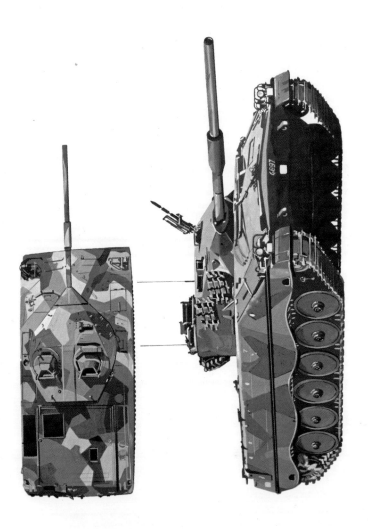

35 Infanterikanonvagn Ikv-91

Sweden

36 Pansarbandvagn
Pbv-302 (*below*) and
155-mm. Bandkanon
1A

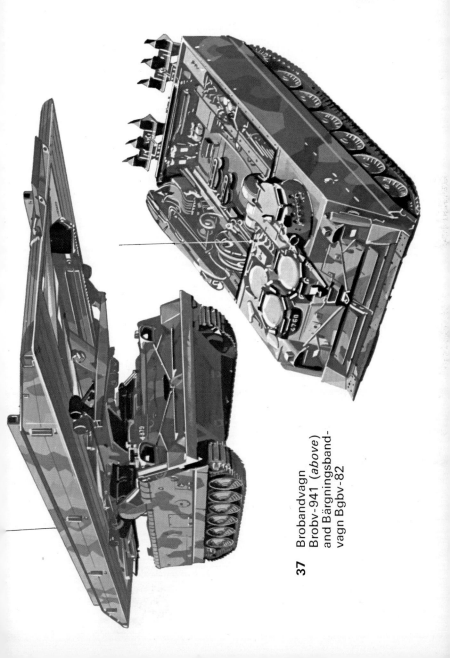

37 Brobandvagn Brobv-941 (*above*) and Bärgningsband- vagn Bgbv-82

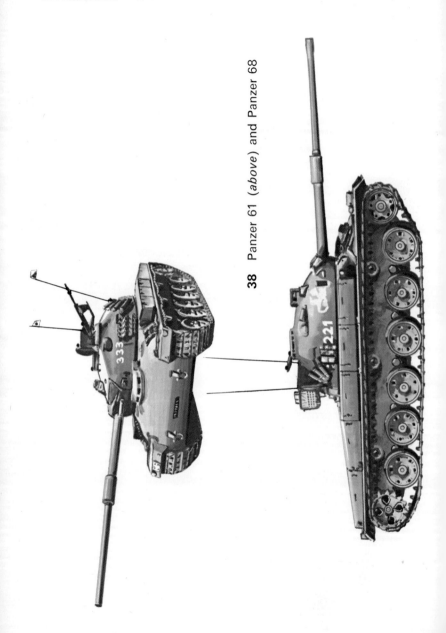

38 Panzer 61 (*above*) and Panzer 68

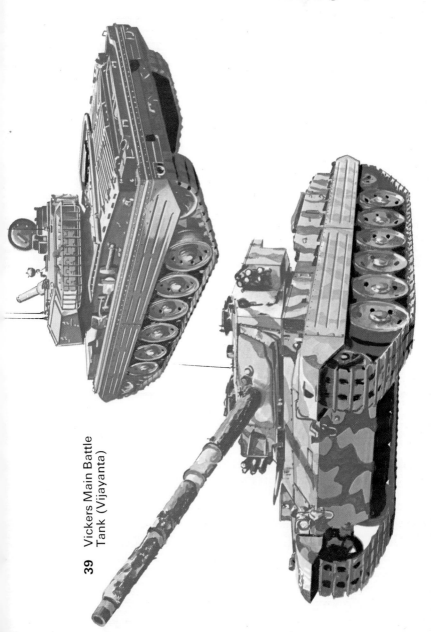

39 Vickers Main Battle Tank (Vijayanta)

United Kingdom

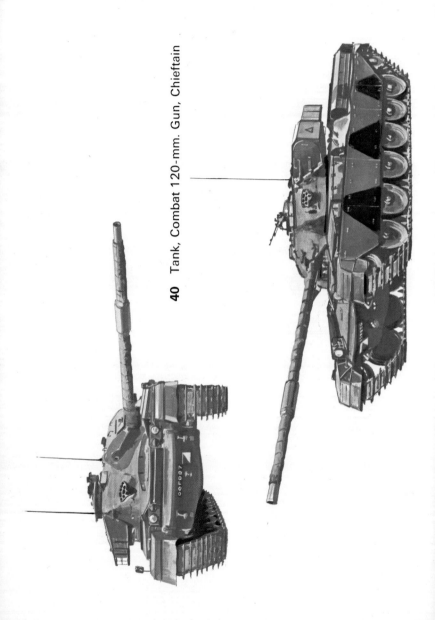

40 Tank, Combat 120-mm. Gun, Chieftain

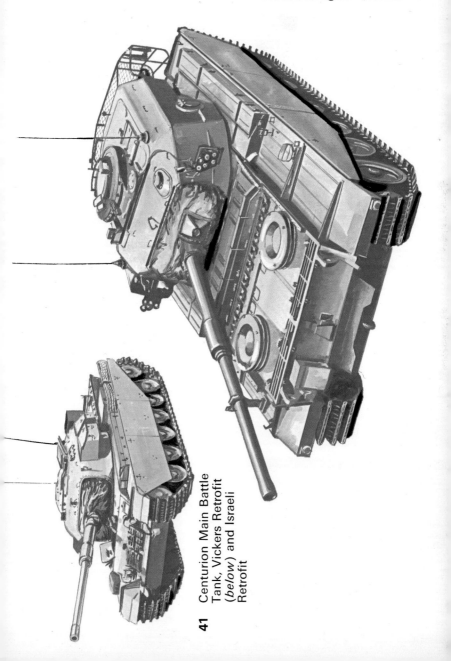

41 Centurion Main Battle Tank, Vickers Retrofit (*below*) and Israeli Retrofit

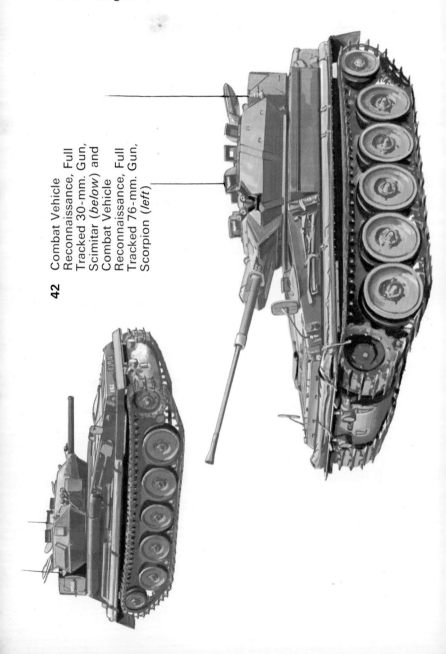

42 Combat Vehicle
Reconnaissance, Full
Tracked 30-mm. Gun,
Scimitar (*below*) and
Combat Vehicle
Reconnaissance, Full
Tracked 76-mm. Gun,
Scorpion (*left*)

43 Combat Vehicle Reconnaissance, Full Tracked,
G.W., Striker (*above*) and Combat Vehicle,
Reconnaissance, Full Tracked, Personnel, Spartan

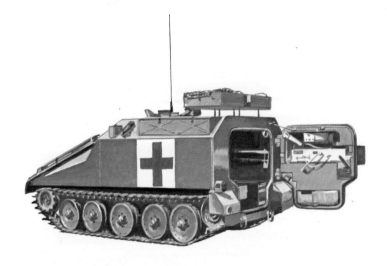

44 Combat Vehicle, Reconnaissance, Full Tracked, Command, Sultan (*below*) and Combat Vehicle, Ambulance, Full Tracked, Samaritan

45 Carrier, Personnel, Full Tracked, FV 432 (*below*)
and Carrier, Maintenance, Full Tracked, FV 434

46 Launcher, Guided
Missile, Carrier
Mounted, Full Tracked,
Swingfire, FV 438
(*above*) and Carrier,
FV 432 with Ranger

47 Gun, Self-Propelled, 105-mm. Fd Gun, Abbot (*above*)
and Falcon, Self-Propelled, A.A. Gun

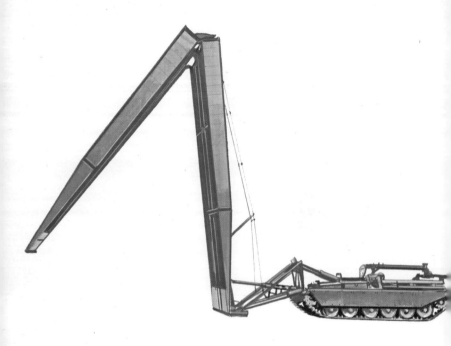

48 Tank, Bridgelayer, AVLB, Chieftain Mk. 5

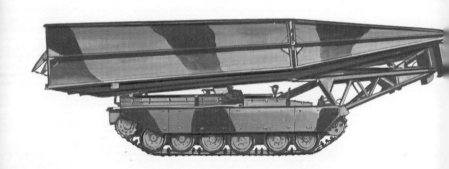

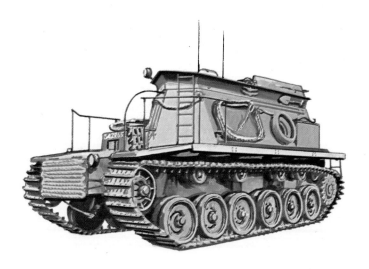

49 Armoured Recovery Vehicle, Beach, Centurion Mk. 5 (*above*) and Armoured Recovery Vehicle, Chieftain Mk. 5

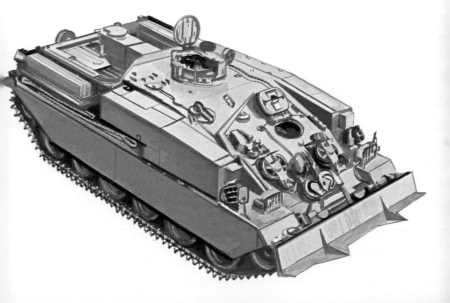

50 Combat Engineer Tractor, Full Tracked

51 Remote Handling Equipment (Tracked) (EOD), Wheelbarrow Mk. 7

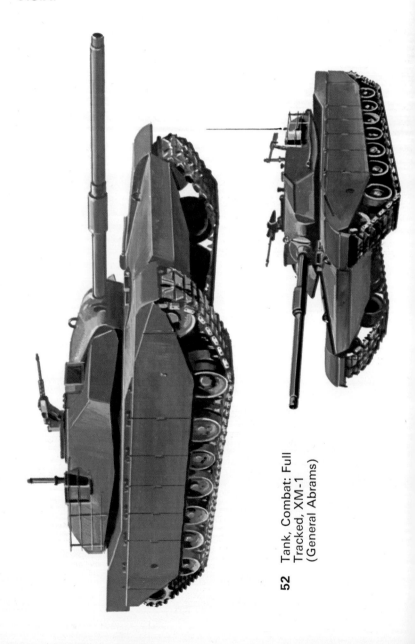

52 Tank, Combat: Full
Tracked, XM-1
(General Abrams)

53 Tank, Combat: Full Tracked, 152-mm. Gun, M-60A2 (*above*) and Tank, Combat: Full Tracked, 105-mm. Gun, M-60A1

U.S.A.

54 Armoured Reconnaissance/Airborne Assault Vehicle:
Full Tracked, 152-mm., M-551

55 Carrier, Personnel: Full Tracked, Armoured, M-113A1 Diesel (*above*) and Carrier, 107-mm. Mortar: Full Tracked, M-106A1

56 Carrier, Command Post: Full Tracked, M-577A1 (*above*) and Carrier, M-113 with Radar

57 Command and Reconnaissance Vehicle (Lynx) (*above*) and Carrier, Command and Reconnaissance, Armoured, M-114A1

58 Landing Vehicle: Tracked-Engineer 7 (*above*) and Landing Vehicle: Tracked-Personnel 7

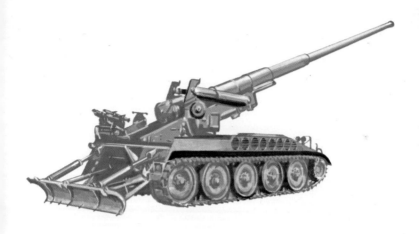

59 Gun, Field Artillery, Self-Propelled: 175-mm. M-107
(*above*) and Howitzer, Heavy, Self-Propelled: 8 inch,
M-110

60 Lance Guided Missile System (*above*) and Howitzer, Medium, Self-Propelled: 155-mm. M-109G

61 Gun, Anti-Aircraft Artillery, Self-Propelled: 20-mm., M-163 (*above*) and Guided Missile System Intercept – Aerial, Carrier Mounted (Chaparral)

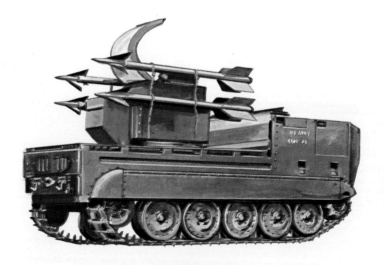

62 Recovery Vehicle, Full Tracked, Medium, M-88 (*above*) and Recovery Vehicle, Full Tracked, Light, Armoured, M-578

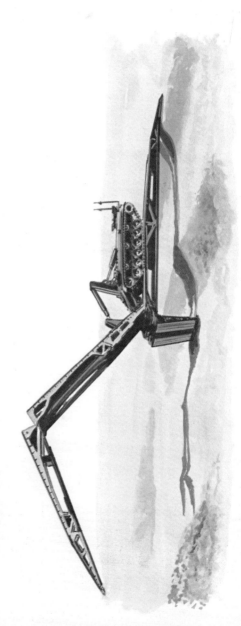

63 Combat Engineer Vehicle: Full Tracked, M-728 (*above*) and Armoured Vehicle Launched Bridge

64 Infantry Combat Vehicle, M-980

TANKS AND OTHER TRACKED VEHICLES
IN SERVICE

1 Tanque Argentino Mediano Argentina (**TAM**), German Federal Republic.

This 30-ton battle tank has been developed by the West German Thyssen–Henschel company under a contract awarded in 1974 by the Defence Ministry of Argentina. The chassis of the Marder infantry combat vehicle has been used as a basis to which has been added a three-man turret mounting a 105-mm. gun. This gun has been developed in Argentina from the French 105-mm. gun used in the AMX 13 and built under licence in Argentina. As the fire control electronic system has also been developed in Argentina, there has been a considerable degree of collaboration between the two countries in the design of this tank, which is to be constructed in factories at Rio Tercero (turret and gun) and Buenos Aires (chassis and final assembly). The initial order is for 200 vehicles.

The maximum weight of 30 tons—similar to that of the World War II Shermans the TAM will replace—was fixed by the Argentine Army. Although it necessarily places limits on the amount of armour protection that can be offered, a vehicle of this weight can be accommodated by most bridges in the country and enables standard commercial heavy trucks to be used as transporters. It also helps to keep down initial and maintenance costs. The six-cylinder diesel engine of the Marder has been uprated to 710 h.p. for the TAM and this gives a high degree of mobility, with a maximum speed of over 75 km./hr.

The 105-mm. gun is stabilized: it has a coaxial 7·62-mm. machine-gun with it in the turret and another machine-gun is mounted for anti-aircraft use. The machine-guns are also made in Argentina, under licence from the Belgian FN concern.

The prototype TAM which was completed early in 1977, and does not have the Argentinian gun, is shown in the illustrations.

Three hundred infantry combat vehicles are also to be built in Argentina. These are a simplified version of the Marder with different firing ports and turret from those of the standard Bundeswehr vehicles.

2 Carrier, Full Tracked, Armoured, M-113A1, Fire Support Vehicle, Australia/U.S.A.

The armoured vehicles with which the Australian Army is equipped are of American, British and German manufacture. However, these are modified to meet special Australian requirements, such as for climatic conditions, and in addition some adaptations have been carried out in Australia itself, partly on grounds of economy.

The American M-113A1 is the standard armoured personnel carrier of the Australian Army and this type has been used as the basis of a local conversion to produce a Fire Support Vehicle for Australian Armoured Cavalry units. The conversion consists of marrying an existing pattern of 76-mm. gun turret to a modified M-113A1.

The first type, which was used by the Australian Army in Vietnam, uses the turret of the British Saladin armoured car. As full depression of the main armament was required, the turret is mounted on a raised ring and, to enable the driver's hatch to be opened without respect to the turret position, the normal hinged type has been replaced with one of a sideways swinging pattern.

The addition of the turret has increased the M-113A1's all-up weight by about 2 tons and has adversely affected the vehicle's stability as well as track and suspension life. The M-113A1 FSV with Saladin turret cannot be air-lifted and care has to be taken in travelling over rough country to avoid overturning and, although the vehicle is amphibious, there would be a risk of capsizing if the turret were turned when in the water.

To overcome some of the above disadvantages, a second version of the M-113A1 F.S.V. has been developed which uses the British Scorpion light tank turret. This lowers the overall height to make the vehicle air-portable in the Lockheed C-130 Hercules and also improves stability on both land and water. The Scorpion turrets are made by Alvis Ltd in the United Kingdom and incorporate Australian detail requirements.

In both models, the armament consists of a 76-mm. gun, a coaxial 7·62-mm. machine-gun, and a second machine-gun mounted on the turret roof for anti-aircraft purposes.

3 Panzerjäger Kürassier, Austria.

The Jagdpanzer Kürassier, or Panzerjäger K, is a tank destroyer using the French FL-12 gun turret on a chassis developed from that of the Austrian Schützenpanzer 4K4FA, described separately.

Designated 4KH6FA, the 'H' probably stands for 'heckmotor' (rear engine) since the principal mechanical change in Kürassier from the Schützenpanzer's layout is that the engine has been moved to the back of the vehicle, and the drive sprockets are also at the rear. The turret, mounted almost in the centre of the vehicle, carries the commander and gunner and is of the oscillating type, with automatic loading for the 105-mm. gun. A rate of fire of approximately twelve rounds per minute can be achieved. An infra-red searchlight for night fighting is in a square container near the rear of the turret roof.

The 105-mm. gun, which has a performance not far short of that of the French AMX 30 battle tank, is a heavy weapon for a vehicle of only 17·5 tons and the armour protection is necessarily limited to little more than the Schützenpanzer's 8–20 mm., except on the turret face, where it is 40 mm. Mobility helps to compensate for light protection, however—the Saurer (Steyr) 6FA six-cylinder diesel engine gives the Jagdpanzer a maximum speed of 67 km./hr.

One hundred and fifteen or more Kürassiers (excluding prototypes) have been built for the Austrian Army by Steyr–Daimler–Puch AG (with guns and turrets supplied from France), and some have been sold to Tunisia. There is also an armoured recovery vehicle version, turretless and with heightened hull, bulldozer blade, crane and winches, known as Bergepanzer Greif, or Bergepanzer K.

4 Schützenpanzer 4K4FA and Schützenpanzer 4K4FA-G, Austria.

Like some of the other smaller neutral countries, not aligned with either the Eastern or Western power blocs, Austria has undertaken a programme of producing some of its own armoured fighting vehicles. It may continue to be more expedient to purchase the heavier A.F.V.s abroad (most of its tanks are either French or American) but the Austrian Army is now equipped with armoured personnel carriers of entirely Austrian design and manufacture.

The Österreichische Saurerwerke AG (which now forms part of the Steyr–Daimler–Puch organization) started work on the design of an armoured personnel carrier in 1956 and the first experimental prototypes were built from 1958 onwards. From these was evolved a vehicle fairly conventional in layout for an armoured personnel carrier, although perhaps owing more to German influence than, say, American practice. The general layout has been retained in successive prototype and production vehicles, which have included a number of improvements.

The Schützenpanzer is a fairly low vehicle, with the engine, transmission and final drive at the front, right of centre, with the driver at the left. The rear compartment (which has twin access doors in the back plate of the vehicle) has accommodation for eight infantry, in addition to the vehicle commander, who occupies a position behind the driver and operates the mounted armament. The basic version (4K4FA) has a 12·7-mm. machine-gun, normally on an open mounting al-

though sometimes a shield is fitted. Alternatively, a turret containing a 20-mm. cannon may be fitted—this model is known as 4K4FA-G.

The suspension on all models consists of five medium-sized road-wheels carried on transverse torsion bars.

In the designation, 4K represents the chassis type and 4FA the engine model, which is a Saurer six-cylinder diesel, developing 250 h.p. Other models with slightly different engine models are 4K4F and 4K3F, and the basic Schützenpanzer is also produced in specialized ambulance, radio, command (three models), rocket launcher and 81-mm. mortar-carrying versions. External differences are not great (although the ambulance, radio and some other versions lack the turret or heavy machine-gun mounting), but some have only a 7·62-mm. MG-42, for which several alternative positions are available, in place of the heavier weapons.

Between 400 and 500 Schützenpanzer (of all models) have been built and are in service with the Austrian Army.

5 Type T-59 Main Battle Tank and Type K-63 Armoured Personnel Carrier, Chinese People's Republic.

Virtually no official information has been released about armoured fighting vehicles built by the Chinese People's Republic, although various types of tank and armoured personnel carrier have been exported by China to Albania and a number of African and Asian countries.

The most widely known Chinese A.F.V. is probably the Type T-59 main battle tank, which is a close derivative and somewhat simplified version of the Soviet T-54. The main details are similar to those of the Soviet tank, although early Chinese versions, at any rate, did not have stabilization for the 100-mm. gun (as, indeed, neither did the earliest Soviet T-54s) and lacked the infra-red headlights and searchlight.

There are also at least three models of lighter tank in service. The Type T-60 is an amphibious tank similar to the Soviet PT-76, from which it has been developed, although the Chinese tank has an 85-mm. gun in a dome-shaped turret more like that of the Type T-59, and is probably heavier. The Type T-62 and Type-63 are also believed to be armed with 85-mm. guns and so all three models may be regarded as reconnaissance vehicles rather than main battle tanks.

The Chinese Armoured Personnel Carrier Type K-63 (or M-1967 or M-1970, as it was previously known for want of a more precise designation) appears to be an entirely original vehicle, as there is no known Soviet or other foreign prototype for it. A smallish vehicle of only about 10 tons with only four road-wheels each side, the Type K-63 has the engine at the front in the centre, and the transmission is to front drive sprockets, with the driver at the left and the commander at the right. A heavy 12·7-mm. machine-gun is mounted on the roof in the centre of the vehicle and appears to be operated from a hatch behind it. The compartment at the rear carries about eight infantrymen, who have access through doors in the rear plate.

A trim vane is carried on the nose plate of the Type K-63 for use in water

when erected. No other preparation is needed for swimming, the vehicle being propelled in water by its tracks.

In addition to the Type K-63, and in production before it, China also uses tracked armoured personnel carriers of the Soviet BTR-50P type.

6 Obrneny Transporter—OT.62 (TOPAS), Czechoslovakia.

The Czech OT.62 (also widely known by its Polish name Transporter Obojzivelny Pasovy Stredni or TOPAS) constitutes an important contribution from the long-standing Czechoslovakian armaments industry to the Warsaw Pact armoury. It is an armoured personnel carrier developed from the Russian BTR-50 PK, over which it is an improvement, having a better performance.

The suspension is similar to that of the PT-76 amphibious tank, to which both armoured personnel carriers owe their ancestry, with six road-wheels each side, sprung on torsion bars. The hull height, compared with that of the tank, is increased to give more headroom for the squad of eighteen infantrymen (plus a crew of two) that can be carried. Although there are various external differences between the Russian and Czech vehicles, the main difference lies in the power unit, which in the OT.62 is a 300-h.p. six-cylinder in-line water-cooled diesel engine.

With armour protection of 10 mm. maximum, the first model of OT.62 had no fixed armament. Model 2 has a small turret with a 7·62-mm. machine-gun mounted at the front right-hand side of the hull, and a later model, the result of Polish–Czech co-operation, the 2AP, has a turret like that of the SKOT eight-wheeled armoured personnel carrier. This turret mounts a 14·5-mm. heavy machine-gun and a 7·62-mm. machine-gun, and the space it takes up is no doubt responsible for the reduction in carrying capacity to twelve men in addition to the crew of three.

The OT.62 has a road speed of about 62 km./hr and is fully amphibious without preparation. Propulsion in the water is by means of two hydrojets at the rear of the hull. A pump, driven by a take-off from the main engine, draws in water through vents in the hull sides and ejects this through the apertures at the rear. A maximum speed of nearly 11 km./hr is possible in water and steering is effected by controlling the volume and direction of the flow from either hydrojet and associated vents.

The OT.62 TOPAS is used by the Czechoslovakian and Polish armies, as well as those of a number of African and Asian countries.

7 Char de Combat AMX 30, France.

The AMX 30 has been developed by France as her main battle tank after careful experiments over 10–15 years with differing layouts of hull and turret design and guns of calibres ranging from 90 mm. to 120 mm.

After the abandonment of the experimental AMX 50, which had a 120-mm. gun in an oscillating turret (like that of AMX 13) and weighed over 50 tons, efforts were concentrated on a much smaller, less conspicuous and more mobile tank of some 30 tons with a conventional turret armed with an unconventional gun of 105 mm. calibre. It was the original intention that this tank should compete for a common design to be adopted by both France and Germany, but ultimately the two countries went their separate ways.

The gun of the AMX 30 is a 105-mm. weapon of unusual design in that although rifled it fires a shaped-charge armour-piercing projectile in which inner rotation is retarded. This weapon thus combines the advantages of the accuracy of a rifled barrel with the high penetration for a relatively small projectile of the shaped charge, which for maximum effect should not be rotated. This projectile, the OCC 105F1, or Obus G, overcomes the problem of spin imparted by the rifled barrel of the gun by the charge itself being mounted on ball bearings, so that rotation inside the casing is so minimal as to have little effect on penetrative performance on impact.

The secondary armament of the AMX 30 consists of a 12·7-mm. heavy machine-gun coaxial with the 105-mm. gun (although it can be elevated 20 degrees beyond that of the 105 mm. for use against aerial targets), and a 7·62-mm. machine-gun mounted on the commander's cupola at the right-hand side, but controlled from inside the tank.

Apart from its armament, AMX 30 follows a layout fairly usual for many modern battle tanks, with medium-sized road-wheels, suspended on transverse torsion bars (although the wheels are, more unusually, of aluminium alloy) and a rear-mounted engine transmitting its power through a five-speed gear-box to track drive sprockets at the rear of the vehicle. The steering system is of the triple differential type, giving varying turning radii according to the gear used. The AMX 30's engine is the Hispano-Suiza HS-110 diesel, water-cooled, with twelve cylinders and develops 720 h.p.

Quantity production of the AMX 30 began about 1965 and over a thousand have been built for the French Army. It has also been supplied to Greece, Venezuela, Chile, Peru, Iraq, Libya, Saudi Arabia and Spain, where it is also being built under licence.

The standard AMX 30 can be fitted with a schnorkel breathing tube for deep wading (this is shown in one of the illustrations, both of which show French Army vehicles) and a simplified 'basic' model AMX 30 is available for export. A family of specialized vehicles is also based on the AMX 30 hull, and some of these are dealt with separately in this volume.

The AMX 30 is to be updated by the substitution of a 120-mm. smooth bore gun, which will use the same ammunition as the German Rheinmetall weapon intended for the Leopard.

8 Char de 13t à Canon de 105 mm. (Char Léger AMX 13) and Bitube de 30 mm. Anti-Aérien Automoteur (AMX 13), France.

One of the most successful light tanks ever built, the AMX 13 has been supplied to over two dozen countries from 1952 onwards and is still in service with the French Army.

The design weight of 13 tons and, to some extent its configuration, was dictated by the original requirement that this tank should be air portable for use by the French airborne forces. Design to meet the specification was carried out by the French fighting vehicle research and development centre Atelier de Construction d' Issy-les-Moulineaux (and hence the initials AMX in the designation of tanks having their origin at this establishment).

A front engine layout, with the driver alongside on the left, with transmission to front-drive sprockets, allowed the turret to be mounted at the rear. This had the advantage of reducing the overhang at the front of the powerful 75-mm. gun that was adopted for AMX 13. The most interesting feature, however, was the use of an oscillating or trunnion-mounted turret. This kind of turret is constructed in two parts, the upper part carrying the gun, which is elevated and depressed with it. This upper part of the turret is mounted on trunnions on the lower part, which rotates on the hull. The oscillating turret simplified fire control equipment and made much easier the installation of automatic loading mechanism by eliminating relative movement between it and the gun mounting.

The AMX 13 entered service with the French Army armed with the long 75-mm. gun Mle. 50 although some tanks had a shorter gun mounted in a Panhard E.B.R. (armoured car) turret. During service with France and the many other countries that purchased the AMX 13 various detail improvements were introduced, and then the 90-mm. gun, firing hollow-charge projectiles, was made available. Conversion to the more powerful gun was carried out on many vehicles in service, including those of the French Army. A further enhancement of the armament, if not the performance of their somewhat heavily loaded chassis, was the addition to the turret of four SS-11 teleguided missiles. Finally, a model with the 105-mm. gun Mle. 57 was introduced. A batch of these have been supplied to the Dutch Army, although earlier models can, if required, be converted to the larger gun.

A specialized tank using the AMX 13 chassis is the 'Bitube de 30-mm. Anti-Aérien Automoteur'. This weapons system, evolved jointly by Direction Technique des Armements Terrestres; S.A.M.M. (responsible for the turret design); Hispano-Suiza (the guns) and Thomson-C.S.F. (radar), consists of a dome-shaped turret mounting the twin 30-mm. cannon, with a rate of fire of 600 rounds per minute each, together with the RD 515 Oeil Noir 1 radar system. The radar can acquire aerial targets up to 15 km. distance and 3,000 metres height and the analog computer of the system provides sight corrections. In addition, 'softskin' or light armoured vehicles can be engaged with direct fire.

This weapons system is in use with the French Army. The same system has been applied also to the AMX 30 chassis, which provides a steadier firing platform and can carry more ammunition.

9 **Véhicule de Combat d'Infanterie AMX 13 and Véhicule de Combat d'Infanterie AMX 10P,** France.

The chassis of the AMX 13 light tank was virtually standardized for a whole family of light support vehicles developed by the French Army in the 1950s and 1960s. The basic vehicle was an armoured personnel carrier (véhicule de transport de troupe—VTT), later redesignated infantry combat vehicle (VCI). This has an unobstructed compartment at the rear with a higher roof than that of the tank. This layout is easily adaptable to ambulance, command, cargo carrying and other functions and can be fitted for carrying and firing various calibres of mortar up to 120 mm., or equipped with a bulldozer blade and a jib as an engineer vehicle.

As an infantry carrier, the V.C.I. AMX 13 can transport a section of twelve men with their personal weapons, in addition to the driver. Totally enclosed, the vehicle was one of the first to provide firing ports to enable the infantry to use their weapons before disembarking. The V.C.I. itself carries a 7·62-mm. machine-gun mounted in a small turret on the top right-hand side of the hull, or a heavy 12·7-mm. machine-gun in an open ring mount in the same position. The Dutch Army has mounted the TOW anti-tank launcher in this location on some of its vehicles.

In addition to the French and Dutch armies, the V.C.I. AMX 13 has also been supplied to Argentina, Italy and Belgium (where it has also been built under licence).

The next generation of French Véhicules de Combat d'Infanterie and associated specialist types is represented by the AMX 10P family. This light armoured vehicle, designed by AMX and manufactured by Groupement Industriel des Armements Terrestres (G.I.A.T.) is able to carry out the functions of the AMX 13 series but has a superior all round performance. As an infantry vehicle, the V.C.I. AMX 10P carries only eleven men including the driver and gunner but, unlike the AMX 13 carrier, is fully amphibious, water propulsion being by means of hydrojets and/or the tracks. The maximum speed on water is nearly 8 km./hr and on roads 65 km./hr. The use of a diesel engine—a Hispano-Suiza Type HS 115, rated at 280-h.p.—helps to give a much greater range of action than the petrol-engined V.C.I. AMX 13—600 km. compared with 400 km. The mounted armament of the AMX 10P consists of a 20-mm. gun and a 7·62-mm. machine-gun contained in a small turret.

The AMX 10P is replacing AMX 13 V.C.I.s in the French Army. Further models in the AMX 10 tracked vehicle range include command, recovery, mortar, 75-mm. gun and HOT anti-tank vehicles, either in production or under development.

10 Obusier Automouvant de 155-mm. AMX 13 and Canon Auto-moteur de 155 mm. GCT, France.

The high cost of modern military equipment means that many armies have two generations of weapons in service simultaneously, and the French 155-mm. self-propelled gun is a case in point.

The 155-mm. gun on the light AMX 13 chassis is classified as 'automouvant' because the crew in action is not fully protected and the weapon can only be fired when the spades at the rear are dug in to help absorb the recoil. The limited space in the vehicle means that only the driver and gun commander can be carried; the remainder of the gun crew and ammunition travel in a supporting vehicle. The gun-howitzer has a maximum range of 21,500 metres on standard ammunition; total traverse is 50 degrees; maximum elevation 67 degrees; and a rate of fire of four rounds per minute can be achieved. Vehicles of this type are in service in Argentina and Venezuela as well as with the French Army.

Although simple and generally effective, weapons of the kind described above are unsatisfactory on a modern battlefield where the ability to seal the vehicle and crew against the effects of nuclear fall out, biological and chemical warfare (N.B.C.) is needed and so development of the 'Canon Automoteur de 155 mm. à grande cadence de tir sur chassis AMX 30' (to give it its full title) began in 1970, the first prototypes being ready by early 1973. Apart from the protection against N.B.C. a weapon with longer range and with automatic loading was required, as well as improved vehicle performance.

The adoption of the AMX 30 chassis enables a fully rotating and fully enclosed armoured turret to be used and the automatic loading system enables a rate of fire of eight rounds per minute—double that of the manually served Automouvant de 155—to be achieved.

The 155-mm. gun has a barrel 40 calibres long; range is 23,500 metres; elevation is 66 degrees and depression 5 degrees; and forty-two rounds of ammunition are carried in the vehicle. A machine-gun is carried for the vehicle's close defence, mounted on the turret roof. The crew consists of commander, gunner and loader, who travel in the turret, and driver who occupies the same position as in the AMX 30 tank.

The Canon Automoteur de 155 GCT is gradually replacing in the French Army not only the Automouvants de 155 but also the 105-mm. weapons in AMX 13 chassis.

11 Véhicule de Tir Pluton AMX 30 and Véhicule de Tir Roland AMX 30, France.

The well-tried AMX 30 chassis has been used for the launcher vehicles of both the Pluton tactical nuclear missile system and the Roland anti-aircraft missile system.

The Système d'Arme Pluton is a means of launching and guiding the surface-to-surface Pluton nuclear missile, which weighs 2,400 kg and has a range of 120 kilometres. It has a simplified inertial guidance system and the missile, propelled by a solid fuel rocket motor, can be fitted with warheads ranging between 10 kilotons and 25 kilotons for ground support or interdiction missions.

The Pluton missile, 7·60 metres long, is carried in a launching container, in which it can be elevated and fired, mounted at the rear of a specially modified AMX 30 chassis, carrying a crew of four. The Command vehicle, also on an AMX 30 chassis, carries the data processing equipment centred on the IRIS 35M computer for identifying the target and firing and controlling the missile, as well as radio equipment for communications over long distances.

The first of five French artillery regiments, each equipped with six Pluton missiles and accompanying equipment became operational in 1974.

The Roland Euromissile as it is called, since it has been developed jointly by Germany and France, is a system intended to combat aerial attack, particularly at low levels and carried out at speeds up to Mach 1·3. The system has been developed in two forms—for all-weather use (Roland 2) and for optical guidance only (Roland 1). The German Bundeswehr uses only the Roland 2, whereas the French forces employ both Roland 1 and 2 in a ratio of about 2 to 1. The Roland 1s can, however, be converted within 48 hours to the all-weather type without difficulty, by addition of the tracking and guidance radar.

Mounted on an AMX 30 chassis, the French version of Roland 1 carries a fully rotating turret with a missile launcher each side and containing the Thomson–CST surveillance radar scanner on top.

In operation, the radar locates and identifies (as an enemy) the target, the vehicle commander centres it on the radar screen, whereupon the aimer (crew member) lines up the target when it comes into vision. The commander then, when the target is within range, activates the firing circuit. The aimer fires the missile and tracks this on to the target by keeping it centred in the optical sights, which include an infra-red tracker sensitive to infra-red emissions from the tail of the missile. This information is processed by a computer which passes corrections to the missile by a microwave transmitter: the signals received are converted into changes in course by the jet deflector in the cruise motor.

Two missiles in their container/launchers are normally carried ready for use, and inside the vehicle are two revolving drums, each carrying four reserve missiles from which they can be automatically loaded.

The AMX 30 Roland vehicle weighs 33 tons and has a crew of three—commander/radar operator, gunner and driver.

12 Char Dépanneur–Niveleur AMX 30D and Char AMX30 Poseur de Pont, France.

Two of the specialized vehicles using the chassis of the AMX 30 main battle tank are an armoured recovery vehicle and a bridge layer.

The recovery vehicle, or AMX 30D, has been designed to recover and/or service battle tanks in or near the battlefield and also to help clear the terrain for them, if necessary under fire. This vehicle, then, carries out functions for which, in the British and German armies, for instance, two different types of vehicle would normally be used.

Operated by a crew of four, the AMX 30D is equipped with a turntable-mounted crane, hydraulically operated, with a lift of 13 tons (or 20 tons when in the forward position only, supported by the stabilizer); a winch driven from the tank's main engine with a pull of 35 tons (also an auxiliary winch for lesser tasks with a 4-ton pull); and a front-mounted hydraulically operated bulldozer blade. This is for clearing obstacles, as a ground anchor for use with the winch,

or as a stabilizer if needed when the crane is in use.

One 7·62-mm. machine-gun for local defence is carried, mounted on a cupola like that of the battle tank; this position is occupied by the crew commander. The vehicle weighs 36 tons, except when (as shown in the illustration) a spare AMX 30 engine transmission assembly is carried on a special frame on the rear deck, when the total weight is 40 tons.

The AMX 30 bridge layer carries a 22-metre bridge, capable of spanning gaps of up to 20 metres wide. The bridge is of the scissors type, pivoted at the rear of the vehicle and rests, when folded, on a rectangular structure (armoured against small arms) on top of the hull, which contains the hydraulic operating jack as well as the commander and bridge operator. The third man, the driver, occupies the normal position in AMX 30 tanks in the left-hand side of the glacis plate.

In operation, the vehicle is backed up to the obstacle, two stabilizers are lowered to take the weight and the bridge is raised upwards and over, unfolding at the same time. The bridge trackway is 3·10 metres wide, but can be increased to 3·92 metres with widening panels.

On the road, the AMX 30 bridge layer weighs nearly 43 tons: its bridge can carry tanks up to 40 tons, or in emergency up to 46 tons.

13 Kampfpanzer Leopard, German Federal Republic.

The Leopard was designed, like the French AMX 30, to meet the requirements of a common main battle tank to replace ageing American equipment in the West German, French and Italian armies. Because of lack of agreement between France and Germany on the time scale of replacement as well as technical differences, the two tank projects went their different ways, Italy eventually adapting the German tank.

After preliminary tests beginning in 1961 between prototypes for the Standardpanzer, as it was called, submitted by two German consortia, the type designed under the leadership of Porsche KG was chosen for further development. Numerous changes and extensive evaluation tests of prototypes were carried out and Krauss–Maffei AG of Munich were appointed as main contractors for the production run. The first Leopard I emerged from the factory in September 1965.

Two fundamental features of the Leopard's design are the 105-mm. British L7A1 gun, chosen for its advantages of standardization with other NATO countries as well as its intrinsic merits, and the Daimler–Benz DB838 830-h.p. ten-cylinder diesel engine, which gives the tank an excellent performance. This transmits power to the tracks by means of a single stage torque converter offering four ratios. The maximum speed is 65 km./hr and the rate of acceleration is also very good: a more rare quality in main battle tanks. The suspension consists of seven road-wheels each side, carried on transverse torsion bars.

The Leopard's 105-mm. gun main armament is supplemented by a coaxial 7·62-mm. machine-gun and another mounted on the turret roof. The crew consists of gunner, loader and commander in the turret (where the commander has duplicate basic driving controls for emergency use) and driver, who sits at the right-hand side of the hull near the front.

Further development of the Leopard continued through production of the initial batches, although the first major change in external appearance occurred with the Leopard 1A3 which has a distinctive angular turret of welded construction, compared with the mainly cast pattern of earlier models.

The welded turret is used on subsequent models, including the A4, which has a fully automatic gear-box and an integrated fire control system, and the Leopard II, in which the hull form has been improved and armament changes, including the proposed 120 mm. Rheinmetall smooth-bore gun, experimented with.

Apart from those supplied to the Bundeswehr, Leopards have been ordered by or exported to Belgium, Norway, Holland, Turkey, Canada, Australia and Italy, where they are also being produced under licence.

14 **Schützenpanzer Marder and Flaraketen Panzer Roland,** German Federal Republic.

Following the traditions of the Panzer Grenadiers of World War II, the German Army began to develop an armoured infantry carrier in the 1950s, using both foreign and German-built vehicles.

Some of the earliest of these were French Hotchkiss carriers (Schützenpanzer kurz) and these were followed by a Swiss Hispano-Suiza design (HS-30, known as Schützenpanzer lang—Spz12-3), which for political and other reasons was produced by Leyland Motors in England, as well as by Henschel and Hanomag in Germany, and used a British Rolls-Royce engine. One of the first German post-war designs for an armoured personnel carrier was the Henschel HWK 11 of 1963, which formed part of a family of light armoured vehicles, which were not, however, used by the German Army although a few were exported.

Experience with the operation of the French and Swiss armoured personnel carriers helped to crystallize German ideas on the subject and the specification for an infantry combat vehicle—as A.P.C.s were to be considered—was drawn up in 1959. Mobility at least equal to that of the main battle tank, a good degree of protection, full use of infantry weapons from the vehicle and a mounted cannon were required. After the testing of three series of prototypes from three different manufacturers, a production contract was awarded to Rheinstahl (an organization which now includes the Henschel firm) in 1969. This long period of development has resulted in a very efficient, if somewhat heavy, infantry combat vehicle.

The Schützenpanzer Marder has an MTU six-cylinder diesel engine of 600 h.p., located at the front behind a long sloping glacis plate, with the driver beside it at the left. A turret containing a 20-mm. Rheinmetall cannon and a coaxial 7·62-mm. machine-gun is mounted on a plinth in the centre of the vehicle and the compartment for six infantrymen (in addition to the

driver, commander and two gunners) is at the rear. A ramp for entry and exit is at the back. Full nuclear, biological and chemical warfare protection is provided.

Besides the standard vehicle, there is a mortar-carrier version and the Marder has been adapted to carry the Roland 2 missile system. This anti-aircraft weapon is as described in the section dealing with the French AMX 30 Roland launcher, except that Roland 2, the only version used by the Germans, has the addition of tracking and guidance radar for all-weather operation. The Roland turret, with its two missile launchers is mounted in the position occupied by the 20-mm. turret in the standard Marder. Ten missiles are carried, two of them ready to fire.

15 **Flakpanzer 1 Gepard and Pantserrups LUA 35 mm.,** German Federal Republic/Holland.

For mobile defence of armoured units in the field against low level air attack in all weathers, the German Army has developed and adopted a weapons system based on the 35-mm. Oerlikon gun and the Leopard tank chassis, and a special version of this, using Dutch radar equipment, has also been accepted by the Dutch Army.

The weapons are two 35-mm. automatic Oerlikon cannon with belt feed, mounted on either side of an armoured turret. The rate of fire is 550 rounds per minute per gun. The guns are allied to a surveillance radar system with a range of up to 15 km, which acquires the target (or targets) and then identifies it as friend or foe. The selected target is then transferred to the tracking radar which can hold it without any movement of the turret being necessary. Calculation of the points of impact is carried out by an analog computer, taking account of the attitude of the vehicle, muzzle velocity of the guns and all other relevant factors. The whole system is superior to many others in that it has the ability to switch rapidly from one target to another.

The version of Flakpanzer I being supplied to the Dutch Army (model 5PZF-C A1, known to the Dutch as Pantserrups LuA 35-mm.) differs chiefly from the purely German version in the radar equipment which, although of comparable performance, is manufactured by Hollandse Signaalapparaten (HSA) on the one hand and Siemens AG on the other. Externally, the Dutch radar system is distinguished by the search radar antenna of cylindrical appearance, while that of the German is rectangular and bowl-shaped. In both types the scanner can be folded for travelling.

The Flakpanzer is operated by a crew of three—commander, gunner and driver. Mechanically, the chassis is closely similar to that of the Leopard battle tank and shares its high degree of mobility.

16 **Kanonenjagdpanzer KJPZ4-5 and Raketenjagdpanzer RJPZ3**, German Federal Republic.

Among the most effective German weapons of World War II were the Sturmgeschütz series of armoured artillery weapons, both field and anti-tank. A modern equivalent, the Kan-onenjagdpanzer, was developed in the late 1950s when prototypes from three different manufacturers were ordered, followed by further prototypes from two of the same firms between 1963 and 1964 and yet again up to 1965, when production orders were finally given to the Henschel and Hanomag companies.

The KHpz 4-5 has a low, fully enclosed hull with a 90-mm. gun mounted in the front of the glacis plate, where it has a traverse of 30 degrees (15 degrees right and left) and elevation of only 15 degrees, since it is intended primarily for anti-tank use. Weighing 25·7 tons, the vehicle is powered by a Daimler–Benz MB 837 eight-cylinder diesel engine, giving it a maximum speed of 70 km./hr. The German Army received 750 of these vehicles and 80 were ordered for the Belgian Army in 1972. The Belgian vehicles are assembled in Belgium and although externally similar to the German version, have improved fire control equipment, transmission and suspension, using components of the Marder infantry combat vehicle.

The Raketenjagdpanzer 2 uses the same basic hull as the Kanonenjagd-panzer and has the same function—combating armour—but uses the alternative method of guided missiles. Production started in 1967 with a version equipped with two launchers mounted on top of the hull for the French-designed SS-11 missile. Fourteen of these rockets are carried: they have an effective range of 3,000 metres. A later version of the Raketenjagd-panzer, RJPz 3 is equipped to launch the later generation anti-tank missile HOT developed jointly by France and

Germany. This weapon has a range of 4,000 metres. Nineteen missiles are carried and there is a single launcher, mounted on the top left-hand side of the hull. Next to it is a periscope from which the missile is aimed and guided. Conversion from the SS-11 to the HOT system has been planned.

17 Bergepanzer 2 Leopard and Brückenlegepanzer 1, Biber, German Federal Republic.

Like most successful main battle tanks, the Leopard has formed the basis of a range of specialized armoured vehicles, including pioneer, recovery and bridgelayer tanks, and self-propelled mountings.

The armoured recovery vehicle, produced by Atlas–MaK Maschinenbau of Kiel, is basically a Leopard in which the turret has been replaced by a low rectangular superstructure and to which a revolving crane and a bulldozer blade have been added. The crane, mounted at the right-hand side of the hull, has a maximum lift of 20,000 kg and can be traversed through 270 degrees. One of its functions is to transfer a complete spare engine from the Bergepanzer's rear deck, where it can be carried, to a Leopard tank during an engine change (which can be effected in 30 minutes). The dozer blade is for stabilizing the vehicle when the crane is used in the forward arc when raising heavy loads, such as a complete battle tank, as well as in earth-moving operations. The other major item of equipment is a winch with a 35,000 kg pull. Many countries as well as Germany using Leopards have also ordered the Berge-

panzer version. The Pionierpanzer is similar in appearance to the Bergepanzer but its equipment includes additionally an auger, operated from the crane jib, for hole drilling.

Two different types of bridge layer on the Leopard chassis were built for experiment. Both models carried a 22-metre bridge mounted over the hull in two sections, the near half (i.e. when laid) on top of the other (distant) half. In the Type A bridge layer the bridge sections were mounted on a pivoted beam, the front of which could be extended over the gap. The bridge, the two halves joined, was then pushed forward along this beam for laying.

In the Type B Bridge Layer the lower (distant) half of the bridge was moved forward from under the upper (near) half to make the complete span, the front of the vehicle being supported on a stabilizing blade. The bridge was then fully extended from a carrying arm in front of the vehicle and laid.

The Type B was chosen for production and entered service with the Bundeswehr in 1973; it is known as Biber (Beaver).

18 Self-Propelled 160-mm. Mortar and Self-Propelled 155-mm. Gun/Howitzer, Israel.

Israel has, through economic necessity, had to get the maximum use out of the military resources available but the country's armaments industry has, nevertheless, managed to produce some effective weapons through the modification of obsolete or obsolescent chassis.

The two vehicles described here are

virtually new designs, although both use the lower hull and running gear of the World War II U.S. M-4A3E8 Medium Tank—Sherman. The armament in both cases is a weapon designed by the Finnish company Tampella and produced under licence by Soltam in Israel.

The self-propelled mounting for the 160-mm. mortar has the weapon mounted with the barrel projecting over the front plate of the hull, which has been increased in height over that of the original M-4A3E8 tank by means of light armour plate. In action, the side and front plates can be folded down to enable the crew to serve the weapon, which has a high rate of fire and a range of 9,600 metres.

The second and more important Israeli S.P. weapon on the M-4A3E8 chassis is the 155-mm. gun/howitzer, which saw action in the October 1973 war. Mounted inside a fixed, welded armour plate casemate with an enclosed roof, the M-68 gun has a barrel 33 calibres long. It has a range of about 20,500 metres and the semi-automatic breech mechanism and pneumatic rammer enables a good rate of fire to be achieved for a weapon of this size. This is four to five rounds per minute for short periods and two rounds per minute for up to one hour. For indirect fire—the normal mode of operation—a panoramic telescope is fitted, together with a normal telescope for direct fire against tanks, for example. Maximum elevation of the guns is 52 degrees, depression 3 degrees and total traverse 60 degrees.

Sixty rounds of ammunition are carried and the vehicle weighs 41·5 tons. One 7·62-mm. machine-gun is carried on the hull roof for defence against ground or air attack. On some vehicles this is mounted in a rotating cupola.

A further version of the 155-mm. gun/howitzer is mounted in a turret with 360 degrees traverse on the British Centurion hull or, alternatively, on American M-47, M-48 or M-60 hulls. This version uses a longer, 39-calibre barrel, which gives it a range of 23,500 metres.

19 **Tank, Type 61, 90-mm. Gun and Tank, Type 74, 105-mm. gun,** Japan.

The Type 61 Main Battle Tank's design was commenced in 1954 when the Japanese Self Defence Force was still almost exclusively equipped with American armoured vehicles, and the layout and general appearance of this tank shows the influence the United States M-47/M-48 tanks had on the Japanese designers.

Sixteen prototypes were built, of which the first pattern (STA-1), ready by early 1957, was lower and more compact than the final version, STA-4, which was standardized in 1961 for production.

The Type 61's gun is a 90-mm. weapon, built in Japan but similar in appearance and performance to that of the American M-48 series with the distinctive transverse tube muzzle brake. This is accompanied by a coaxial 7·62-mm. machine-gun, and a heavy 12·7-mm. machine-gun is mounted on the commander's turret hatch.

With a crew of four and weighing

35 tons, the Type 61 follows the long tradition in Japanese tanks of using an air-cooled diesel engine. This is a twelve-cylinder V unit built by Mitsubishi developing 600 h.p., which gives a maximum road speed of 45 km./hr.

Some 450 Type 61 Main Battle Tanks are estimated to be in service with the Japanese Self Defence Force.

The design of the Type 74 Main Battle Tank makes full use of the fact that the average Japanese soldier is less tall than his Western counterpart and so this tank is much lower and more compact than all other turreted main battle tanks, with the advantage of offering a smaller target and making concealment easier. This asset is further increased by the hydropneumatic suspension system, whereby the ground clearance can be adjusted from 60 cm down to 20 cm.

Designated STB, several different prototype versions were built, of which the first two vehicles, known as STB-1, were completed in September 1969. STB-1 featured a semi-automatic loading system for the British-designed 105-mm. L6 gun, although this feature was dropped in later prototypes on grounds of economy. The last prototype, STB-6, was finished in 1973 and this model incorporated all the final features of the Type 74 Main Battle Tank, production of the first 280 of which had already commenced in 1972 at the Tokyo Machinery works of Mitsubishi Heavy Industries.

The Type 74 uses a compact two-stroke ten-cylinder V-form diesel engine, developing 750 h.p. The maximum road speed is 53 km./hr, but the vehicle's overall mobility has been

considered to be of the greatest importance. The hydropneumatic suspension enables a good cross-country performance to be sustained with the minimum crew fatigue, and water up to a depth of 1 metre can be forded without preparation. Complete submersibility is possible with the use of 'schnorkel' tubes for the engine exhaust and the tank commander.

Full stabilization for the 105-mm. gun is fitted and the weapon is controlled by a laser range-finder together with a ballistic computer, so increasing the probability of a first-shot hit on the target. Two machine-guns are carried: one 7·62 mm., coaxial with the main gun, and a 12·7-mm. anti-aircraft weapon mounted on the turret. There are also six launchers (three either side of the turret) for smoke or anti-personnel grenades, and the crew are protected against nuclear fall-out and biological and chemical warfare.

20 **Armoured Personnel Carrier, Type 60, and Armoured Personnel Carrier, Type 73,** Japan.

Among the earliest vehicles to be developed in Japan for the Japanese Self-Defence Force to replace American equipment were a range of armoured carriers: what might be called the 'standard' vehicle of the earlier series (although not the first to be developed) is the Type 60 Armoured Personnel Carrier.

Prototypes known as SU-1 and SU-2 were submitted by Komatsu and Mitsubishi respectively in 1957. The Mitsubishi vehicle was selected for further development and eventually went into production by Mitsubishi Heavy Industries and entered service as the Type 60 Armoured Personnel Carrier.

Fully enclosed and carrying eight men in addition to the crew of two, the Type 60 has an eight-cylinder diesel engine of 220 h.p. which gives it a maximum speed of 45 km./hr. A fixed armament of one 7·62-mm. machine-gun in a ball mount in the front glacis plate and a 12·7-mm. machine-gun on a ring mounting is carried.

The successor to the Type 60 is the Type 73 Armoured Personnel Carrier, which has the performance required of an infantry combat vehicle of the 1970s. Also designed and produced by Mitsubishi Heavy Industries, this vehicle makes use of aluminium armour so, although larger, with capacity for ten men in addition to the crew of two, and with a much better performance than the Type 60, it is only about 2 tons heavier.

A maximum road speed of 60 km./hr can be attained, powered by the air-cooled 300-h.p. two stroke diesel engine, which also propels the vehicle by its tracks in water. The Type 73 has full nuclear fallout, biological and chemical warfare protection and has infra-red equipment for night driving and combat. The armament consists of a ball-mounted 7·62-mm. machine-gun in the front glacis plate and a heavy, 12·7-mm. machine-gun mounted on the right-hand side of the hull roof, either in a turret or in an open ring mounting.

Type 73s are gradually replacing the Type 60s in infantry regiments of the Japanese Self-Defence Forces.

21 Self-Propelled 106-mm. Recoilless Gun, Type 60, and 4.2-in. Mortar Carriage, Type 60, Japan.

The first armoured vehicle developed for the Japanese Self-Defence Force was, appropriately, a self-propelled anti-tank weapon. Design work of the vehicle—the model SS—commenced in 1954; prototypes were submitted by Komatsu and Mitsubishi (SS-1 and SS-2 respectively) and after trials and some fusion of ideas further prototypes (SS-3 and SS-4) were built. The contract for the standardized vehicle, the Self-Propelled 106-mm. Recoilless Gun, Type 60, was awarded to the Komatsu company.

An interesting vehicle that has few parallels in other armies, other than the U.S. M-50 Ontos (now obsolete) and some experimental vehicles, the Type 60 is a small self-propelled mounting for two 106-mm. recoilless guns. These weapons are mounted on the right-hand side of the vehicle, with the crew at the left—the commander and loader behind the driver. The guns, in their mounting, can be raised, together with the commander's cupola, in which position they have a traverse of 30 degrees right and 30 degrees left of centre. They are breech loaded and a rate of fire of six rounds per minute can be achieved, although the projectiles are bulky and only ten are carried. The guns can also be fired from the low position, although the traverse is then limited to 10 degrees left and 10 degrees right. In this configuration, the vehicle is only 1·38 metres high and very inconspicuous, although in action this asset is offset by the prominent back-blast of the recoilless guns.

The thin-tubed guns are rifled and fire hollow charge anti-tank and high explosive rounds. The effective range is 1,100 metres and ranging is by means of a 12·7-mm. heavy machine-gun controlled by a range-finder and optical sight.

An air-cooled six-cylinder diesel engine of 120 h.p. mounted at the rear gives the Type 60 SPRG a maximum speed of 48 km./hr.

A specialized development of the Type 60 Armoured Personnel Carrier (described separately), the 4·2-in. Mortar Carriage, Type 60 (model SX), is closely similar to it, and uses the same engine, transmission and running gear and even the hull, apart from the rear portion, is basically the same.

At the rear of the mortar carrier is the compartment containing the 4·2-in. (107-mm.) mortar, from which it can be fired. For travelling, the roof of this compartment is covered by upward- and sideways-opening hatches.

For its own protection, the Mortar Carriage carries a 12·7-mm. machine-gun on the roof although, unlike the Type 60 Armoured Personnel Carrier, the machine-gun on the glacis plate has been eliminated.

22 Armoured Vehicle Launched Bridge, Type 67, and Self-Propelled 155-mm. Gun (HSP), Japan.

For the usual reasons of economy and rationalization, Japan has produced a range of support vehicles using the same chassis as, or many components of, current main battle tanks. These include armoured recovery and armoured engineer vehicles as well as the bridge layer and S.P. gun described here.

The bridge layer uses a turretless Type 61 battle-tank chassis with relatively slight modification. The bridge (some 12–13 metres long when extended) is of the scissors type, first introduced by the British during World War II. The laying process is similar to that of the U.S. M-60 AVLB: the folded bridge is raised, the weight taken up by a stabilizer in front of the tank, and then opened out and placed over the gap.

American-built self-propelled guns formed the first equipment of the post-war Japanese Self-Defence Force and in the 1950s there was a Japanese experimental S.P. 105-mm. howitzer which did not enter production. The model HSP is entirely Japanese in design— both vehicle and gun—although, like other S.P. guns of its class, it shares a general layout in common with the widely used American M-109 155-mm. S.P. gun.

Mounted in a fully enclosed turret at the rear of the vehicle, with 360 degrees traverse, the 155-mm. gun has an elevation of 65 degrees and depression of 5 degrees. This arrangement requires forward placing of the 420-h.p. two-stroke diesel engine and, although the same tracks, elements of the running gear and hull components of the Type 74 Main Battle Tank have been employed, the transmission is through front track sprockets. This is the reverse of that in the Type 74, although, more unusually for a modern Main Battle Tank, the earlier Japanese Type 61 used front drive. A heavy (12·7-mm.) machine-gun is mounted on the turret roof for the vehicle's defence.

Weighing 24 tons, the 155-mm. S.P. gun has a maximum road speed of 50 km./hr. The crew consists of six men, all of whom are in the turret except the driver, who is at the right-hand side of the hull in front of the turret.

The S.P. gun has been developed by by Japanese Ministry of Defence in conjunction with Mitsubishi Heavy Industries, by whom it is built, at their Tokyo Machinery Works.

23 T-72 (Main Battle Tank), Soviet Union.

Few details of the latest Soviet main battle tank have been made available despite the fact that over 800 are in service in East Germany and that over 2,000 are estimated to have been produced. Even the designation, variously reported as T-64 or T-72 (although more likely to be the latter) is not known with certainty at the time of writing.

An experimental tank, known as T-70, followed the T-62 and appears to have been used to test out ideas to be used in the definitive successor to the T-62. The T-70 has a 115-mm. gun, like that of T-62, but with the addition, it is believed, of an automatic loading device. The calibre of the T-72's very long gun is, however, between 122 mm. and 125 mm. and it fires fin-stabilized rounds. The small cast turret with near-vertical sides would seem to confirm reports that the gun has automatic loading, with four rounds ready for use and twenty-eight more in the loader. There is the usual 7·62-mm. coaxial machine-gun and a 12·7-mm. machine-gun on the commander's cupola.

A crew of only three is carried— driver, gunner and commander. The latter is at the right-hand side of the turret (contrary to earlier Soviet practice), the gunner at the left and the driver in the centre of the hull, just in front of the turret.

The suspension of the T-72 consists of six road-wheels each side, smaller than those of T-62, with track return rollers. The engine is thought to be a diesel of around 900–1,000-h.p. to give a maximum road speed, in the vehicle of around 40 tons, of 60 km./hr.

24 T-62, (Main Battle Tank), Soviet Union.

A further step in the systematic evolution of the Soviet main battle tank, the T-62 retains many of the main characteristics of the T-54/T-55 series, although it has a 115-mm. calibre gun for only a relatively slight increase in weight and overall dimensions.

The 115-mm. gun is a high velocity smooth-bore weapon, firing fin-stabilized projectiles, of which forty are carried, including high explosive as well as armour-piercing rounds. The gun is fully stabilized in both vertical and horizontal planes. The larger gun requires a larger turret ring than that of T-55 and this has led to an increase in width of just over a quarter of a metre and in length of just over half a metre, although the height (to turret top) has been kept down to the 2·4 metres of the earlier tank.

A twelve-cylinder V water-cooled diesel engine developing 700 h.p. is used in the T-62, which gives the same maximum speed as the T-55 of 50 km./hr, with probably an improved overall performance.

First seen in public in 1965, the T-62 has been built in large numbers and supplied to the Soviet Union and Warsaw Pact armies to supplement or replace T-54s and T-55s. It has also been provided for a number of African and Middle East Countries and is likely, in time, to replace earlier Soviet tanks at present employed by many other armies.

25 T-55 (Main Battle Tank), Soviet Union.

Although made obsolescent by further advances in design, the T-55 is still an effective fighting vehicle, and the sheer numbers of this tank still in service make it an important one.

Derived from the famous T-34 of World War II, through the interim models T-44 and T-54, which it closely resembles, the T-55 was first shown publicly in 1961 and possibly entered service a year or so earlier. The T-54, which first began to come off the production lines some twelve years before T-55, has been progressively improved through several models but the final changes in the basic design which resulted in the T-55 were principally in the engine and transmission and the gun stabilization equipment.

The power plant of the T-55 is an improved model twelve-cylinder V water-cooled diesel, developing 580 h.p. (compared with T-54's 520 h.p.), resulting in a slightly better performance. The transmission has been improved to match the increased output

and the fuel capacity has been raised to give a 25 per cent. better radius of operation. The T-54 (except for the earliest models) had the 100-mm. gun stabilized in elevation/depression only, but T-55 has stabilization in both vertical and horizontal planes, making accurate shooting on the move easier. The ammunition supply has been increased by nine rounds.

The layout of the T-54/T-55 series is fairly conventional for modern main battle tanks, with the engine and transmission at the rear of the hull (with rear track drive sprockets), the driver at the front left-hand side and the fighting compartment and turret, containing commander, gunner and loader, in the centre. The suspension consists of five largish road-wheels each side, carried on transverse torsion bars.

Common to both T-54 and T-55 is the armament of a 100-mm. gun with coaxial 7·62-mm. machine-gun and another fixed machine-gun (fired by the driver) in the front of the hull. The latter has, however, been omitted from the final models of T-55.

The turret of the T-55 has been evolved from that of T-54, which has a ventilation dome near the front of the roof and originally had cupolas for the loader as well as the commander. Late model T-54s have one cupola only— like the T-55, which also has no turret ventilator dome. An anti-aircraft machine-gun is carried on some, but not all, models of both T-54 and T-55.

A compact and reliable tank, the T-55, together with the T-54, has been produced in large quantities in the Soviet Union (and possibly also in Poland and Czechoslovakia) and supplied to over two dozen countries in addition to being used by the Warsaw Pact armies.

26 PT-76, Amphibious Tank, and ASU-85, Airborne Assault Gun, Soviet Union.

The PT-76 (PT = Plavayushchiy Tank, or amphibious tank) is a reconnaissance tank, air-portable and amphibious, that first appeared about 1950. Since then it has been supplied to some twenty countries outside the Soviet Union and is still widely used.

Weighing 14 tons, the PT-76 has full amphibious capability, the only preparation needed being the erection of a trim board, which is hinged at the junction of the glacis plate and the nose plate. In water, the tank is propelled by twin hydro-jets, the outlets for which are in the rear vertical plate of the hull. The hydro-jets are operated by a pump driven from the main engine. Steering in water is by means of the hydro-jets in conjunction with two extra vents, one on either side of the hull, towards the rear above the track guards. Ten km./hr can be attained in smooth water: on land the maximum road speed is 44 km./hr.

The driver in the PT-76 occupies a central position in the hull just forward of the turret. He is provided with three periscopes for closed-down vision on land and an extra extendable periscope for use on water, to enable him to see over the raised trim board. The commander and gunner are in the turret, which is set well towards the front of the vehicle and contains the armament of one 76·2-mm. gun and, coaxial with it, one 7·62-mm. machine-gun. Only on the final version of the PT-76 is the 76-mm. gun fully stabilized. The PT-76's engine is at the rear: it is a six-cylinder in-line water-cooled diesel of 240 h.p. and the drive is to rear track sprockets. The suspension consists of six medium-sized road-wheels carried on torsion bars.

A Polish-used PT-76 is shown in the illustration.

Successor to the much smaller and less powerful ASU-57, the ASU-85—which appeared in public for the first time in 1962—is the principal Soviet airborne assault vehicle. Based on the chassis of the PT-76 tank, the ASU-85 has the same engine, transmission and running gear and is approximately the same weight. It is not amphibious, however, and the hull form has been adapted to its different role as an assault gun and tank destroyer. The 85-mm. gun (which fires high explosive as well as armour-piercing rounds) is located just left of centre of the long-sloping glacis plate, where it has a total traverse of 12 degrees, elevation of 15 degrees and, like many Soviet A.F.V.s, a very limited depression of 4 degrees. The driver is to the right of the gun, the other three crew members (commander, gunner and loader) behind, and the engine at the rear.

Only 2·1 metres high, the ASU-85 can be transported by air and also parachute dropped. The illustration shows an ASU-85 bearing typical Soviet Airborne forces markings.

27 BMP-1, Infantry Combat Vehicle, and BMD, Airborne Combat Vehicle, Soviet Union.

The BMP-1 belongs to the second generation of armoured personnel carriers from which the infantry carried can use their small arms and have turret-mounted weapons effective against armour.

Perhaps one of the best vehicles of its kind in service, the BMP-1 is highly mobile, fully amphibious without preparation and has a low profile although (as in many Soviet A.F.V.s), this is to some extent at the expense of crew comfort. Built of light alloy armour and weighing only 12·5 tons (only half that of the German Marder), the BMP-1 has a crew of three and can carry eight infantrymen. The engine, a six-cylinder water-cooled diesel developing 280 h.p., is located at the front and can produce a maximum road speed of 55 km./hr, or 8 km./hr in water, when propulsion is by means of the tracks. Many components of the BMP-1 are in common with the PT-76 tank.

The mounted armament consists of a 73-mm. smooth-bore gun with automatic loading, firing fin-stabilized anti-tank or high explosive rounds, and a 7·62-mm. machine-gun in the turret and a launcher for the 'Sagger' (NATO name) anti-tank guided rocket on brackets, over the 73-mm. gun. Both gun and 'Sagger' are capable of penetrating heavy armour, the latter at longer ranges up to 3,000 metres.

The BMP-1 is in service with the major Warsaw Pact countries as well as several Arab countries. An East German vehicle is shown in the illustration.

Although the BMD (Boyevaya Mashina Desantnaya) looks like a miniature version of the BMP-1 it was, in fact, designed for a wider role with the airborne forces—as a light tank for mobile fire support and protection against enemy armour, as well as to carry a limited number of infantry. Weighing around 8·5 tons, this little vehicle is some 5·3 metres long and is only lightly armoured, but carries the same offensive armament as the BMP-1. In addition to the crew of three, up to six infantrymen can be carried—in very cramped accommodation. The vehicle shown is carrying the markings of the Soviet Airborne Forces as it appeared in a parade in Moscow.

28 ZSU-57-2, Anti-Aircraft S.P. Gun, and ZSU-23-4, Anti-Aircraft S.P. Gun, Soviet Union.

The Soviet Union, like other countries, has turned from guns to mobile missile systems to combat medium- to high-flying aircraft, while adhering to multiple quick-firing small-calibre cannon, usually radar controlled, to protect armoured columns from fast, low-flying machines.

The ZSU-57-2 is one of the older generation of S.P. A.A. guns, although it is still in service with fifteen countries, albeit probably only in second-line employment in the Soviet Union itself and its principal allies. Consisting of two 57-mm. guns in an open-topped turret on a shortened T-54 tank chassis, this vehicle was first shown to the public in 1957. The guns have an elevation of 85 degrees, and an effective range of 4,000 metres against aerial targets, although they are also usable against armoured vehicles or personnel, with appropriate ammunition. The commander and the four members of the gun crew are in the turret and the driver is situated at the left front of the hull. The engine is the same as that of the T-54 battle tank and the suspension and running gear is similar, but with one less road-wheel each side. The maximum road speed of the ZSU-57-2 is the same as the T-54's but the reduced weight of 28 tons results in a generally better overall performance.

As used by the Soviet Army, the ZSU-57-2 is a purely visual weapon and does not appear to have been up-dated by the addition of radar, although some of the other user countries may have done so.

The ZSU-23-4 on the other hand is fully operational in a wide range of visual and climatic conditions, being equipped with radar for both target acquisition and fire control, as well as normal optical sights. The quadruple 23-mm. cannon have a high rate of fire of up to 1,000 rounds per minute for each gun, although for normal use the rate is about 200 rounds per minute. The effective range against aircraft is up to about 2,500 metres. The radar can acquire targets up to 20 km. distant and the system enables the cannon to be armed and fired while the vehicle is moving.

The ZSU-23-4's layout and crew locations is roughly similar to that of the ZSU-57-2. The lower chassis and running gear is practically identical to the PT-76's and the engine and trans-mission are believed to be the same. The performance is also like that of the PT-76, although the ZSU-23-4 is not amphibious.

In service with about as many different countries as the ZSU-57-2, the ZSU-23-4 is replacing the earlier self-propelled weapon in the front line units of the major Warsaw Pact armies.

29 **SU-122, Self-Propelled Gun,** Soviet Union.

A comparatively late addition to the armoury of the Warsaw Pact nations, this armoured self-propelled field artil-lery piece was first shown in public in 1974, development having taken place over several years before this. The 122-mm. self-propelled mounting with a revolving turret is an innovation, as far as Soviet equipment is concerned—all earlier such guns having been in fixed mountings—but has a similar configur-ation to the American M-109, which may have inspired its design. There is also a 152-mm. howitzer mounting on a somewhat similar chassis.

Few details are available, but the suspension is similar to that of the Ganef missile carrier which, in turn, is derived from that of the PT-76 family. The engine of the SU-122 is at the front with the driver alongside it at the left. The turret, containing the com-mander and gun crew is at the rear; a position to facilitate loading of am-munition etc.

Both illustrations show vehicles of the Polish Army, one of the users of the SU-122.

30 **SA.6 Gainful, Anti-Aircraft Missile Carrier, and Straight Flush, Armoured Fire Control Vehicle,** Soviet Union.

The Surface to Air (SA) system known by the NATO code name of Gainful or SA-6 is a highly mobile and flexible weapon that has been given the credit for destroying over one-third of the

Israeli aircraft lost in the 1973 Arab–Israeli war.

A medium-range anti-aircraft weapon (the SA-4 Ganef covering greater ranges up to 70 km. and the SA-7 Grail (a hand-held or vehicle-mounted launcher) and ZSU-23-4 dealing with short distance and close up aircraft) intended for dealing with attacking aircraft at ranges between about 5 km. and 30 km., the Gainful consists of three rockets mounted on a fully rotating turntable carried on a chassis derived from that of the PT-76 tank.

The SA-6 is a 6·2 metres long, single-stage missile, launched by a solid fuel rocket engine and propelled in cruise (at approximately Mach 2·5) by a liquid fuel ram jet. Its warhead is of the high explosive fragmentation type. The command guidance system is in the centre section and there are receiver antennae and beacons on the tips of the two rear fins.

The carrier vehicle has the automotive characteristics and general performance (although it is not amphibious) of the PT-76, on which it is based.

The Gainful system has been supplied by the Soviet Union to other Warsaw Pact armies as well as those of several other countries, including Egypt and Syria. The illustration shows a vehicle in Egyptian colours: the supports for travelling under the forward part of the rockets have been lowered and the missiles have been elevated about 5 degrees in the first stage of preparation for action.

The Straight Flush (NATO name) fire control vehicle used in conjunction with the Gainful system has a similar chassis to that of the missile carrier. The target-tracking radar and the target acquisition radar are both mounted on a pedestal in the centre of the vehicle, the tracking radar on top. In action, the Straight Flush would usually receive the target information from a long-range radar (such as Flat Face (NATO name), mounted on a truck) and by means of its acquisition radar, after pinpointing it and identifying it as friend or foe, pass it to the tracking radar to lock the system on to the target so that a missile can be launched.

31 Frog 5, Missile Carrier, and SA-4 Ganef, Anti-Aircraft Missile Carrier, Soviet Union.

FROG is the NATO name for the Soviet battle-field support rocket, or Free Rocket over Ground. A tactical surface-to-surface (SS) weapon, Frog 5 is the final type of its series to have a tracked carrier-launcher, the later models being transported on eight-wheeled high-mobility trucks.

The earliest model, Frog 1, was mounted on a JS-3 tank chassis, but Frog 2 (first seen in 1957), Frog 3, Frog 4 and Frog 5 have all used a chassis based on that of the PT-76 reconnaissance tank, although differing from it in many ways. The Frog 2's chassis was the closest to its parent vehicle's design but later models have had track support rollers added, and a lowered front idler, as well as a different pattern of road-wheels. The engine and transmission are similar to that of PT-76 and Frog's performance (excluding amphibious capability) is still roughly comparable to that of the reconnaissance tank.

In all the tracked Frog series, the rocket is carried over the vehicle's hull, in a girder-structure launcher, pivoted towards the rear, with a bracket on the glacis plate for support when travelling.

The unguided artillery rockets are estimated to have ranges between about 20 and 50 km., according to model. They are of the two-stage solid propellant type (except for Frog 2, which was single stage) and can be fitted with nuclear, high explosive, chemical or bacteriological warheads. In length they range from about 10·5 metres for Frog 3 and 4 down to about 9·5 metres for Frog 5. The later type, Frog 7, is even shorter, but of increased diameter. The crew of the Frog 5 missile launcher and its carrier is three to four men.

The self-propelled anti-aircraft missile system bearing the NATO code name of Ganef, SA-4 or SAM-4 (Surface-to-Air-Missile) was first shown to the public in Moscow in 1964. Two missiles on a launcher are carried over the hull of a special tracked vehicle. This vehicle is unlike any other known earlier tank or armoured vehicle and, with engine and transmission concentrated at the front, leaving the rear end clear for the launching equipment, may have been specially designed for its task. It is air-portable.

The Ganef missile is about 9 metres long and is propelled by an internal ram jet after being lifted off by the four solid propellant boosters, mounted externally. It is operated in conjunction with a scanning radar, and the Pat Hand (NATO name) target acquisition and fire control radar are carried in separate vehicles. The system is intended for medium- to long-range targets up to about 70 km.

32 SS-14 Scamp (Scapegoat) and SS-15 (Scrooge), Strategic Missile Carriers, Soviet Union.

These monstrous Soviet long-range ballistic missiles are both carried on tracked chassis, although later carriers for this kind of weapon seem likely to be heavy wheeled vehicles.

The SS-14 missile is carried in a cylindrical container mounted on the carrier vehicle. Preparatory to launching, the container is raised hydraulically and placed in the vertical position on a launch pad lowered from the rear of the vehicle. The container is then opened, and moved away, leaving the missile ready for launching. An intermediate range missile with a nuclear warhead, the SS-14 is about 10·7 metres long, is propelled by a solid fuel rocket, and has an estimated range of 3,500 km.

The SS-15 intercontinental ballistic missile, which is about 18·3 metres long, is carried on the vehicle in a tube, from which its nuclear warhead projects. Erected in a similar way to the SS-14, the SS-15 is believed to be fired direct from the carrying tube. Propelled by a solid fuel rocket, it has a range believed to be about 5,600 km.

The carrier vehicles Scamp for the SS-14 or Scapegoat system and Scrooge for the SS-15 (all names and designations are those given by NATO, since the Soviet nomenclature has not been made public) are similar to each other mechanically, although the missile erecting systems differ in detail, and the very much longer and heavier SS-15 missile needs extra supporting brackets, which project from the front hull of its carrier. In both vehicles, the running gear is made up from components of the JS-III tank or, more likely, its later derivative the T-10 heavy tank. The carriers have eight smallish road-wheels each side (JS-III had six, T-10 had seven) sprung on torsion bars. The long upper track run is supported on five track rollers each side, unevenly spaced. Power transmission is via rear track sprockets and the engine is assumed to be a V-12 cylinder diesel similar to that of T-10, developing 700 h.p. In both types of vehicle the crew travel in a superstructure at the extreme front, which is unarmoured or only lightly armoured.

33 T-54/MTU, Tank Bridge Layer, and T-54/PT, Tank Mine Clearer, Soviet Union.

Relatively little use was made of specialized armoured vehicles—such as the range developed by the British Army—by the Soviet Union in World War II. The Russian Commanders were reputedly prepared to sacrifice if necessary a whole tank battalion to clear a minefield by the quick but costly method of sending the tanks straight across it. Since 1945, however, a variety of attachments and modified Soviet tanks for special tasks have appeared. It is perhaps significant that some of these vehicles have been developed in the Warsaw Pact countries, such as Czechoslovakia and the German Democratic Republic. Bulldozer and snowplough blades can be

fitted to standard main battle tanks with slight modification and armoured recovery vehicles (including several models designed in the G.D.R.) are based on turretless T-54 or T-55 tanks.

The standard Soviet tank bridge layers all use T-54 or T-55 chassis (which, being turretless, are not readily distinguishable from each other) although T-62 chassis are likely to follow in the same role. One of the most widely employed versions of the MTU, or Mostoukladtschik Tankowje Ustrojstwo, is the T-54/MTU shown in one illustration. This vehicle carries a bridge with a span of 12 metres. A single rigid lattice structure, the bridge is supported on brackets over the hull of the tank. The front brackets project some 2-3 metres in front of the vehicle and the bridge is pushed forward over these supports when being launched.

Another type of bridge layer has a box-construction type of bridge carried in a similar way, but the two shorter end sections are folded over the main sections for transport. Opened out, the bridge has a span of about 19 metres: it is launched in a similar way to the type described above, but a stabilizing spade, mounted at the front of the tank is needed to take the much greater weight at launching.

A third type of bridge layer, developed in Czechoslovakia, has a bridge of about 18 metres. This is carried folded and is of the 'scissors' type, opening out for launching when the front supporting bracket is lowered to the ground to act as a stabilizer.

Both plough and roller devices for mine clearing are employed by the Warsaw Pact countries. A Czech-designed plough for use with T-54 or

T-55 tanks has a plough blade, capable of uprooting and turning aside mines in the vehicle's path. There are several patterns of anti-mine rollers in use, of both Soviet and Czechoslovakian design. The T-54/PT (Protivo Tankoviy) shown in the illustration, has two heavy spiked rollers, towed behind a frame projecting in front of the tank. Each roller is made up of three pinion wheels, side by side, and can roll a lane wider than the tank's tracks. It weight should be sufficient to detonate any normal anti-tank mine.

34 Stridsvagn Strv. 103B, Sweden.

Credit for the most completely original approach to the design of a modern main battle tank must be given to Sweden for the S-tank, or Stridsvagn 103 as it is known in service.

Three important—and often conflicting—criteria to be taken into account in a battle tank are an effective gun (in which the possibility of a first time hit on an enemy tank and a good rate of fire are highly important); the maximum practicable degree of protection (and overall size, minimizing the target offered, is relevant here); and mobility—notably speed in traversing the battlefield, changing position and, not least, getting out of action quickly when necessary.

These criteria have been met in a tank having the unusual combination of a low turretless hull with an automatically loaded, rigidly mounted gun, traversed and elevated by movements of the vehicle itself. Motive power is provided by the combination of a diesel engine with a gas turbine engine.

Independent experiments were conducted from the 1950s onwards with a range of different chassis, to test the viability of systems for elevating a gun by altering the attitude of the hull in which it was mounted; for means of traversing a tank chassis to a fine degree for gun aiming in the horizontal plane; and automatic loading systems to take advantage of a gun fixed in relation to the tank hull. Before the actual S-tank prototypes were built, test rigs for a hydro-pneumatic suspension and steering system were constructed.

The firm of AB Bofors was entrusted with the design of the new tank, in conjunction with the Swedish Army Ordnance tank design section. The first prototype, which appeared in 1961, contained all the essentials of the new design. A low compact vehicle, the gun —a 105-mm. weapon of British design but built in Sweden with an increased barrel length of 62 calibres—projects from the centre of a long sloping glacis plate. There are four roadwheels each side (these are of the Centurion type, to simplify spares problems), rear idler wheel and front driving sprocket. The two engines and transmission are under the glacis plate with the crew behind them, either side of the gun—the driver and radio operator back-to-back on the left and the commander on the right. The radio operator is provided with a basic set of driving controls to enable him to drive the tank backwards in emergency. Commander and driver both have a set of driving and gun controls (which are integrated) so either can drive the tank and fire the gun or exchange roles in case of necessity. The automatic loading equipment is at the rear of the tank where it can readily be reloaded through two hatches in the rear plate. The automatically loaded gun can achieve a rate of fire of fifteen rounds per minute—about twice that of a manually served gun of the same calibre. Fifty rounds are carried. The secondary armament consists of two fixed 7·62-mm. machine-guns located in an armoured box on the left side of the glacis plate, and there is also a machine-gun mounted externally on the commander's cupola.

The idea of a dual diesel and gas turbine engine system was derived from warship design where the diesel is used for cruising, with the gas turbine there to provide supplementary bursts of power for short periods when needed. In a tank the extra advantage of an alternative source of power, should one engine or the other be knocked out or fail in an emergency, is even more marked and, in Swedish winter conditions, the use of a gas turbine to start the diesel in low temperatures is an added advantage. The S-tank's diesel engine is the six-cylinder Rolls-Royce K-60 of 240 h.p. and the gas turbine was originally the Boeing 502-10MA of 330 h.p. on the Strv.-103 Type A, all of which have now been replaced by the Boeing 553 of 490 h.p. (produced in Belgium by F.N. under licence). Tanks with the 490-h.p. gas turbine are designated Strv. 103B. A maximum speed of 50 km./hr can be achieved.

A bulldozer blade to help the tank dig itself in can easily be added to the nose plate, and a flotation screen for swimming is carried folded in an armoured trough round the hull sides.

The S-tank is in service only with the Swedish Army. Some 300 have been built and although it has also been tested by other armies (perhaps because its design is so revolutionary), it has not so far been adopted elsewhere.

35 Infanterikanonvagn Ikv-91, Sweden.

Although having many of the characteristics of a light reconnaissance tank, the Ikv-91 has been specifically designed for infantry support—a role previously filled in Swedish service by vehicles of the German Sturmgesschütz variety. However, complete rethinking by the Swedish Army of its requirements for armoured fighting vehicles has resulted in a vehicle which can, in fact, carry out a much more versatile role than its immediate predecessors.

A design by AB Hägglund & Söner was chosen from among fourteen submitted and the first of three prototypes was completed by the end of 1969. Development proceeded fairly rapidly, so that the first production vehicles began to be delivered to the Swedish Army in 1975.

As the ability to operate in the difficult forest and lake country of north Sweden was required, amphibious capability without preparation was called for in the Ikv-91. This has been achieved by the adoption of a relatively wide and roomy hull in a vehicle weighing only 15·5 tons. Armour is necessarily light, but the maximum effective frontal protection is given by a long sloping glacis plate and a low, well-profiled turret. The tracks have been redesigned from an existing type to give longer wear in sandy soil and extra thrust when propelling the vehicle in water, where 7 km./hr can be attained.

The Ikv-91's gun is a Bofors-designed lightweight, low recoil 90-mm. weapon of the low pressure type, firing fin-stabilized projectiles, including armour-piercing and high explosive rounds. Although the gun can be fired on the move, it is perhaps more likely to be used from cover. It is not stabilized but has an advanced fire control system, including a laser range-finder, an automatic drift calculator, sensors to measure wind and atmospheric conditions, and a ballistic computer which processes all the information fed into it. Two 7·62-mm. machine-guns are carried—one coaxial with the 90-mm. gun and one externally on the loader's turret hatch.

A commercial-type Volvo Penta six-cylinder in-line diesel engine of 294-h.p. is used in the Ikv-91, mounted diagonally at the rear. This arrangement both decreases the space it takes up and simplifies the transmission. A maximum road speed of 64-km./hr can be attained. The vehicle has a crew of four—the driver at the front left-hand side and the commander, gunner and loader–radio operator in the turret.

6 Pansarbandvagn Pbv-302 and 155-mm. Bandkanon 1A, Sweden.

The Swedish Army relied for a number of years on a type of armoured personnel carrier rebuilt from the chassis of obsolete Strv M/41 tanks, which were the Czech TNH built under licence. Fitted with new engines and with an entirely different upper hull, these armoured personnel carriers, Pbv 301, were virtually new vehicles. An economical expedient, these carriers were highly successful in many ways. The limits imposed by the size of the original chassis, however, and the desire for a fully purpose-built armoured personnel carrier led to AB Hägglund & Söner, who had produced the Pbv 301, being asked in 1961 to design its successor.

The Pbv 302, which appeared in prototype form late in 1962 and as a production vehicle in 1966, has a layout very much like that of the American M-113. Unlike the U.S. vehicle, however, the Pbv 302 was designed to carry a 20-mm. gun turret: this is mounted on top of the hull at the left side near the front. The driver sits next to the turret in the centre and the vehicle commander is to the driver's right. The engine—a Volvo commercial six-cylinder diesel of 270 h.p.—and transmission are under the floor beneath the feet of the three front crew members. Up to nine infantrymen can be carried in the compartment at the rear, to which two doors in the vehicle's back plate give access. Roof hatches enable the infantry to use their personal weapons so, together with the turret, the Pbv 302 has the main characteristics of much later mechanized infantry combat vehicles.

An unusual feature is the double skin hull, which increases buoyancy, improves protection against hollow charge missiles and the opportunity has been taken of giving the outer skin a shape to lessen water resistance. The Pbv 302 can attain a speed of 8 km./hr in water, driven by its tracks and has a maximum road-speed of 65–70 km./hr.

The 155-mm. Bandkanon 1A is a weapon—both gun and its self-propelled mounting—designed and built by AB Bofors. Earlier known as VK-155, this self-propelled gun was developed during the 1950s, a production order was awarded in 1965 and all the vehicles (supplied only to the Swedish Army) were completed by 1968.

Mounted in a turret with limited traverse (a total of 30 degrees), the 155-mm. gun, 50 calibres long, has maximum elevation of 40 degrees. Loading is (apart from the first round) carried out automatically from a magazine holding 14 rounds. A jib mounted over the turret allows the magazine to be replaced from a supply vehicle in only two minutes. The rate of fire of the gun is 14 rounds (a full magazine) per minute, and the maximum range is 25,600 metres.

Many mechanical features used in the Bkv 1A are shared with the S-tank, including elements of the suspension and a similar transmission and dual engine arrangement. At 53 tons, however, the Bkv 1A is the heaviest Swedish armoured vehicle and with the relatively low speed of 24 km./hr and lacking amphibious capability it does not share the performance of most other Swedish A.F.V.s.

37 **Bärgningsbandvagn Bgbv-82, and Brobandvagn Brobv-941,** Sweden.

These two Swedish support vehicles share the same basic chassis, which also has many mechanical elements used in the earlier Pbv 302 armoured personnel carrier and the Ikv 91 infantry gun vehicle which followed them.

Intended to serve as an armoured recovery vehicle for units equipped with the Strv 103 battle tank ('S-tank') as well as the much lighter Pbv 302, the Bgbv 82 was designed by AB Hägglund & Söner, work started in 1966, the prototype appeared in 1968 and production commenced in 1970. In order to enjoy the advantage of greater mobility, including amphibious qualities for the standard armoured recovery vehicle, the decision was taken that actual battlefield recovery of S-tanks under fire should be undertaken by other S-tanks. This enabled the armour protection and weight of the Bgbv 82 to be kept down so that the desired mobility characteristics could be attained.

The Bgbc 82 has the front part of the hull fully enclosed, to give armour protection to the crew of four when travelling. For defence it has a turret, mounted at the left, containing a 20-mm. cannon. The rear compartment, which is open, contains the engine (a six-cylinder Volvo-Penta diesel of 310 h.p.) and transmission (at the left), the crew working area, the lifting crane (capable of a 5,500 kg lift with 1·5-metre jib or 1,500 kg when extended to 5·5 metres), the hydraulic winch motor, and other recovery equipment. Two ground anchor spades and two stabilizers on common brackets are positioned on the rear plate of the hull for use with the winch (the cable of which runs through a guide in the centre of the rear plate) and the crane respectively. The winch can exert a 20-ton pulling force or 60 tons in a triple-part pull. A bulldozer blade is carried on the front of the vehicle.

The armoured bridge layer Brobv 941 is likewise intended to serve vehicles up to and including the S-tank: in fact, the bridge's capacity is 50 tons, suitable also for Centurion tanks.

The hull of the bridge layer is closely similar to that of the armoured recovery vehicle, including enclosed protection for the crew of four men, although it lacks the 20-mm. gun turret, having a pintle-mounted machine-gun instead. The automotive characteristics and performance are also much the same as that of the Bgbv 82 including, more unusually in a bridge layer, the amphibious ability. For water crossing, the bridge, which is of box construction and buoyant, is towed by the laying vehicle.

The bridge is carried on the vehicle supported by a girder which is mounted on a bracket located just behind the crew compartment. For launching, the girder is extended by hydraulic means across the gap. The bridge, which is 15 metres long, is then run forward across the girder and lowered to touch ground on the other side of the gap. The girder is then withdrawn, placing the near end of the bridge on the ground, and returned to the horizontal position over the vehicle. A bulldozer blade is carried on the front of the bridge layer to help in preparing, if necessary, the approach ground for the bridge.

38 Panzer 61 and Panzer 68, Switzerland.

The Swiss Army has traditionally been provided with its small arms and light weapons largely from Switzerland's own armaments industry. The first tanks, however, were purchased abroad, but the difficulty during World War II of obtaining further supplies of armoured vehicles led to the first steps being taken to design and produce armoured vehicles in Switzerland. No great progress was made and foreign tanks were again purchased between 1951 and 1960—notably 200 French AMX 13 light tanks and a total of 300 British Centurions of various Marks. During this time, the desire for greater self-sufficiency in A.F.V.s and reduction of expenditure abroad, coupled with the Army's wish to have a main battle tank designed for Swiss conditions, led to the decision to undertake the development of a tank.

Before the armament was finally decided on, a small number of tanks was completed armed with a Swiss 90-mm. gun and these were known as Panzer 58. By the time of their completion in 1961, however, the British 105-mm. tank gun had been perfected and this was to be adopted not only for the Centurion—in both new and up-gunned versions—but also for the United States' M-60. This gun, then, was chosen for the Swiss tank, not only on its merits, but, no doubt, with the attractive possibility in mind of rearming the Swiss Centurions and so achieving standardization.

The new tank, named Panzer 61, exhibited several interesting features, the outstanding of which were its comparatively light weight of 38 tons and its compactness. These points aid mobility in a country in which well over half the terrain is mountainous but has an efficient rail network.

The hull of the Pz61, apart from its narrowness, achieved in part by the location of the diesel fuel tanks either side of the driver, with 105-mm. rounds stored between them, is unusual in being cast largely in one piece. As well as being a means of producing heavy armour within the capabilities of Swiss industry, this enables a good ballistic profile to be achieved. A second feature, and one contributing to the overall compactness, is the adoption of a Belleville washer suspension. The Pz 61 is one of the few tanks to use this system. Each of the six road-wheels each side is suspended independently on a nest of these conical springs, mounted outside the hull.

The turret, which is also cast, contains the 105-mm. gun. This gun is made in Switzerland under licence and has a modified breech block and its mounting allows for increased recoil, lessening the stresses in a tank much lighter than most others in which it is installed. Mounted with the gun in the turret is a 20-mm. Oerlikon cannon. A 7·5-mm. machine-gun is mounted on the loader's turret cupola, at the left-hand side.

As a suitable Swiss engine was not available, the German-built Daimler-Benz MB.837, a V-8 cylinder diesel of 630 h.p., was adopted. This is linked to a Swiss SLM gear-box and a double differential steering system with a hydrostatic steering drive. This power unit gives the tank a maximum speed of 55 km./hr.

One hundred and fifty Panzer 61s were built for the Swiss Army—to equip three tank battalions—and were delivered between 1964 and 1966. When it was decided in 1968 to order a further

170 tanks, the opportunity was taken of introducing improvements in the design. Designated Panzer 68, the new model is very similar in appearance and layout to its predecessor, the most obvious difference being in the substitution of a coaxial 7·5-mm. machine-gun for the 20-mm. cannon. Less obvious are modified idler wheels, redesigned tracks and aluminium, instead of steel, road-wheels. Much more important, though, is the addition of a hydroelectric stabilization system for the 105-mm. gun.

The engine of the Pz68 is an uprated version of the Daimler-Benz diesel, giving an extra 30-h.p. and increasing the maximum speed of the tank to 60 km./hr.

The Swiss have also developed a range of support vehicles (some only in prototype form) using components of the Pz61 and Pz68 battle tanks. These include the Panzerkanone 68 (a S.P. 155-mm. gun), Entpannungspanzer 65 (armoured recovery vehicle) and Brückenpanzer 68 (bridge layer).

39 Vickers Main Battle Tank, (Vijayanta), United Kingdom/India.

Designed as a private venture by Vickers Ltd, the Vickers Main Battle Tank, or 37-ton tank as it is sometimes called, was intended to incorporate the hitting power of the Centurion in a lighter, more simple, tank, suitable to the needs of some overseas countries.

Using the 105-mm. gun, by then current in the Centurion, the Vickers M.B.T. has roughly the Centurion's layout but is over 10 tons lighter mainly through the acceptance of a lower degree of protection, both hull and turret being built up from welded rolled steel armour plates, rather than the more usual castings.

A good degree of mobility has been provided for by the use of the Leyland L.60 engine and transmission adapted from those designed for the 52 ton Chieftain. With output restricted to 650 h.p. the reliability is improved and the Vickers M.B.T. still has a top speed of 56 km./hr. The suspension of the Vickers tank differs from that of both Centurion and Chieftain in that the six road-wheels each side are carried on transverse torsion bars. Unusual additions to this system are secondary torsion bars for the first, second and last pairs of road-wheels, which come into action to absorb the greater wheel action encountered in these positions, where there are also hydraulic dampers.

To help compensate for its relatively light protection by British standards (80-mm. maximum on hull and turret, which is only between half and three-quarters of that on later Centurions), the Vickers M.B.T. has an advanced gun control and stabilization system, which enables its gun to be laid while on the move and fired very quickly after the tank halts or, in emergency, even fired while on the move. The 105-mm. gun is ranged by means of a heavy 12·7-mm. machine-gun, mounted next to it—a system which has advantages over optical range-finders in conditions of cross-winds or poor light, for example. Both the ranging machine-gun and a coaxial 7·62-mm. machine-gun for general use are mounted to the left of the main weapon and a second 7·62-mm. machine-gun can be mounted on the commander's cupola, which is at the left-hand side of the turret roof.

The Vickers Main Battle Tank went into production in India, where it is known as Vijayanta (Victor) in 1966. This followed tests of a Vickers-built tank in 1965 and delivery of many components for the Indian production line at Avadi, near Madras. The number of British-made components has subsequently been considerably reduced for the Indian Vijayantas, of which over 500 are believed to have been built.

An order for 50 Vickers Main Battle Tanks was placed by Kuwait in 1968 and the first tank was delivered early in 1971.

A Mark II version of the Vickers M.B.T. was armed with four Swingfire anti-tank guided missiles added to the turret sides in addition to the regular armament. This has not gone into production in England or India, as far as is known, but existing tank models could obviously be modified to this standard if required.

Various other improved versions of the Vickers M.B.T. have tentatively been called Mark III, the earlier of which (in scale model form only) had a new turret with a cast, rounded front part, and a cast hull glacis plate, greatly improving protection. Later, a version of the M.B.T. with basically standard hull and turret has been equipped with a General Motors 800-h.p. twelve-cylinder diesel engine in power pack form.

Provision is made in the design of the Vickers M.B.T. for a nylon flotation screen to be carried, folded, in a trough at upper track-guard level. This can be erected in 15 minutes: water speed, propelled by the tracks, is 7 km./hr. This equipment does not, however, appear to be carried as standard by either Indian or Kuwait M.B.T.s.

40 Tank, Combat 120-mm. Gun, Chieftain, United Kingdom.

The Chieftain was introduced to replace both the Centurion and the Conqueror as Britain's main battle tank. Conqueror was a support tank for Centurion and had a 120-mm. gun but weighed 65 tons (bridge group 80). It was, in fact, the heaviest tank then in service in the world and although heavily armoured, its mobility was low and the maximum speed was only 21 m.p.h. The Centurion was still a very good tank but it was desired to keep ahead of future Soviet tank developments by putting a 120-mm. gun in a tank at least as well protected as Centurion while keeping weight down to 45 tons, although early design studies for the new tank made it necessary to increase this figure to 51·8 tons.

The Chieftain's general layout is that common for most main battle tanks of the 1970s—the engine at the rear, the fighting compartment and turret in front of it and the driver in the hull at the front. One unusual feature in the Chieftain, however, is that the driver occupies a semi-reclining position when the tank is closed down. This enables the hull height to be kept down, reducing weight and, by decreasing the overall size of the target, improving invulnerability.

A new turret design was adopted for Chieftain in which the mantlet was eliminated. This also helped to reduce weight, to help compensate for the 120-mm. gun, which was and is more

powerful than those of the majority of main battle tanks in service which, in general, rely on guns of smaller calibre with hollow charge projectiles for their penetrative effect. Apart from the range and accuracy of the heavy rifled barrel, it can penetrate most forms of armour on current battle tanks, including the spaced plates which offer protection against hollow-charge projectiles. As the loading system is manual, for such heavy ammunition projectile and charge are separate but, nevertheless, a rate of fire of up to 10 rounds per minute (for short periods) can be attained. The gun is ranged by means of a 12·7-mm. (0·5-in.) heavy machine-gun in conjunction with optical sights, although a laser range-finder coupled with a digital computer is under development. A 7·62-mm. machine-gun, coaxial with the main gun, is also mounted in the turret, and another is carried on the turret cupola of the commander and can be aimed and fired by him from inside the turret.

A multi-fuel engine, basically a diesel but able to operate on a wide range of different liquid fuels in accordance with NATO requirements, was developed by Leyland Motors (now British Leyland) for the Chieftain. This engine, the Leyland L60, is a compact twelve-cylinder vertically opposed type, developing, in late versions, 750 h.p. The original models of this engine gave only 585 h.p. and were rather unreliable but successive improvements have been made, many of which have been incorporated retrospectively in earlier vehicles, to enhance reliability as well as increase performance.

The Chieftain's suspension is similar to that of Centurion, namely the modified Horstmann type consisting of road-wheels in three pairs each side, sprung on three horizontal springs to each pair of wheels. The maximum road speed of 48 km./hr is lower than that of most contemporary main battle tanks and is at the expense of the Chieftain's corres-pondingly better protection. It is claimed, however, that cross-country mobility—which in most tanks is often limited by the endurance of the crew—compares quite well with tanks of other countries. There is no provision for Chieftain to swim, but deep wading is possible with the use of schnorkel breathing equipment.

There are eight basic Marks of Chief-tain, and numerous sub-types: few external differences are apparent, al-though many improvements have been made since the tank first went into service in 1966.

As well as forming the main tank equipment of the British Army the Chieftain has been ordered by Kuwait and is being produced in large numbers for the Government of Iran. The first Iranian orders were for a total of 857 tanks of a version known as Chieftain Mk. 5P. Later vehicles, to a reported total of 1,200, will be of an improved type of Chieftain called Shir Iran (Per-sian Lion) using the laminated protec-tion known as Chobham armour and a new Rolls-Royce twelve-cylinder diesel engine of 1,200 h.p.

41 Centurion Main Battle Tank, United Kingdom.

Although its basic design goes back as far as 1944, the Centurion is a rugged and, even by today's standards, quite well-protected tank, which rearmed to modern standards has proved that it can still give a good account of itself. With further improvements, such as to in-crease mobility and range, it is superior to many tanks designed decades later.

The Centurion has a general layout which became common in World War II and has continued for the majority of main battle tanks ever since: driver at the front, fighting compartment and turret in the middle and engine com-partment at the rear. The Centurion's track drive is to rear sprockets and the suspension is of the modified Horst-mann type. This system, which con-sists of the road wheels being mounted in three sets of two each side, sprung on horizontal springs, lacks some of the advantages of the popular independent transverse torsion bars of today, but it does have the merit of not taking up floor space inside the hull.

The engine chosen for the Centurion was the twelve-cylinder Meteor of 600/650 h.p., which was derived from the famous Rolls-Royce Merlin aero-engine, used for R.A.F. fighters. The Centurion's original gun was the 17-pdr (76·2 mm.)—the most effective British tank gun of World War II. By the early 1950s the 20-pdr (83·4 mm.) gun had been introduced and this was, in turn, superseded in 1961 by the Vickers L7A1 105-mm. gun—a weapon that was to be adopted by the U.S.A., Germany and many other countries and is still one of the most widely used tank guns.

Centurions have been supplied to sixteen different countries and many are still in active employment. They were used on both sides in the Arab–Israeli wars and were still effective in the

1973 battles. This was perhaps the more so with the Israeli Centurions because of the modifications that had been carried out on them to improve their performance.

The Israeli Centurions were of different Marks and were obtained from different sources, but all are believed to have been standardized on armament with the Vickers 105 mm.—as, indeed, have Israeli U.S. M-48s of different models and captured Soviet T-54s and T-55s. Some Centurions, however, have been completely reworked with a new 750-h.p. Continental diesel engine, coupled with a new gear-box and steering system and other improvements. This has helped to increase the maximum speed from about 35 to 45 km./hr, as well as improving general mobility and range.

Vickers Ltd, the present 'design parents' of the Centurion, have offered their own rework scheme to bring older tanks up to the same or higher standard as the Israeli Centurions. The Vickers Centurion Retrofit Programme includes the following features: a General Motors V-12 cylinder diesel of 715 h.p. in power pack form to replace the Meteor petrol engine; modified final drives; TN 12 semi or fully automatic gear-box (as used in the Chieftain and Vickers Main Battle Tank); up-armouring of the glacis plate; fitting 105-mm. gun (on early models with 17-pdr or 25-pdr gun); modernized gun control equipment and/or adding laser range finder; improved commander's cupola; adding nuclear, biological and chemical warfare protection; fitting night vision equipment. Some or all of the above items can be supplied or fitted as required and, if necessary,

tanks can be completely overhauled and many detail improvements effected. The Swiss Army, which had 150 early Centurions equipped with the 20-pdr gun, has had some of its tanks refitted in accordance with this programme.

42 Combat Vehicle Reconnaissance, Full Tracked 76-mm. Gun, Scorpion and Combat Vehicle Reconnaissance, Full Tracked 30-mm. Gun, Scimitar, United Kingdom.

The Scorpion light tank was developed to meet a British Army requirement for a tracked air-portable reconnaissance vehicle. To enable it to tackle main battle tanks, if necessary, in fighting reconnaissance missions or for support in airborne operations a 76-mm. gun, firing a range of ammunition suitable against armour or infantry, is carried.

Developed by Alvis Limited (part of the British Leyland organization) in conjunction with the Military Vehicles and Engineering Establishment of the Ministry of Defence, the six-cylinder Jaguar car engine was adopted for Scorpion, giving the advantage of a well-tried and successful engine, coupled with economy in production and development. Derated from its normal output of 265 h.p. to 195 h.p., the Jaguar engine gives the Scorpion a maximum speed of 81 km./hr and a rate of acceleration that, for a tracked vehicle, can bear comparison with that of the Jaguar sports car.

A weight of just under 8 tons is achieved partly by the use of aluminium for the construction of the Scorpion's hull and turret. The engine is located near the front of the hull at the right-hand side, with the driver beside it at the left, and the seven-speed semi-automatic gear-box and final drive system is in front of them. The concentration of the automotive elements in this way, with front drive to the tracks, has left the rear of the vehicle completely clear for the fighting compartment, a layout that has enabled the Scorpion chassis to be used readily for a variety of other vehicles, some of which are described separately in this book. The suspension consists of five road-wheels—also made of aluminium—each side, sprung on transverse torsion bars. The turret, mounted over the fighting compartment, containing the commander and gunner, has the 76-mm. gun (with elevation of 35 degrees, depression 10 degrees) and a coaxial 7·62-mm. machine-gun, which can be used for ranging the main gun. Between forty and sixty rounds of 76-mm. ammunition are carried, the higher figure when the Nuclear, Biological and Chemical protection pack is not fitted in the rear of the fighting compartment. Scorpions supplied to countries with hot climates have a special air conditioning system fitted. Belgium shares in the production of the Scorpion and its family of vehicles and it is employed in her army as well as the British Army and those of several African and Asian countries.

The need was felt for a tracked vehicle to complement the Scorpion, with the same general characteristics, but with an automatic gun of smaller calibre and a much larger ammunition supply, effective against light armoured vehicles and 'soft skin' vehicles. This requirement has been met by the Scimitar, which has a 30-mm. Rarden

cannon, mounted (together with a 7·62-mm. machine-gun) in a modified Scorpion turret. The Rarden gun, named after the Royal Armament Research and Development Establishment and the Enfield (Middlesex, near London), Royal Small Arms Factory, where it was jointly developed, is an automatic weapon, capable of firing at a maximum rate of 100 rounds per minute, in bursts of up to six rounds. Single shots are also possible for 'sniper' fire. British-designed or Hispano 30-mm. ammunition can be used, and 165 rounds are carried. Although only lightly armoured or unarmoured targets are normally envisaged, the British APDS-T round is capable of penetrating the sides of main battle tanks. With an elevation of 40 degrees, the Rarden cannon, although not intended in Scimitar as an anti-aircraft weapon, can be used at least as a deterrent to helicopters.

Because of their compact hulls, although light in weight, Scorpion and Scimitar lack sufficient buoyancy for swimming, but both can be made amphibious by means of a flotation screen carried folded round the hull just above track level. This can be erected in under 5 minutes: water speed, propelled by the tracks, is approximately 6½ km./hr.

43 Combat Vehicle, Reconnaissance, Full Tracked, Personnel, Spartan and Combat Vehicle Reconnaissance, Full Tracked, G.W., Striker, United Kingdom.

The chassis of the Scorpion light tank proved readily adaptable as the basis of a family of light armoured vehicles, one of which is the Spartan armoured personnel carrier. Engine and driver are at the front, as in the Scorpion, but the hull at the rear is increased in height, providing accommodation for four men and their personal weapons and equipment, in addition to the commander whose position is on the right, immediately behind the engine. The rear compartment has a door at the back, observation periscopes at either side and hatches from which the crew can fire their personal weapons. The gunner (who also acts as radio operator) is behind the driver and operates a 7·62-mm. machine-gun, which is mounted externally on the gunner's cupola and can be aimed, fired and reloaded from under cover. Spartan is slightly heavier than Scorpion but has practically identical performance characteristics, including the amphibious capability with the use of screens.

The Spartan is highly mobile but as the number of men carried is relatively few, compared with the FV 432, it is not normally used as an infantry personnel carrier but rather for reconnaissance or engineer assault teams. It can also be used as a specialized load carrier, such as for demolition stores, or Swingfire missiles for Striker vehicles.

The Striker Anti-tank Guided Weapon carrier is basically the same vehicle as the Spartan but the rear compartment is occupied by the Swingfire equipment. The three front crew positions are the same as in the Spartan, except that the commander is behind the driver and operates the 7·62-mm. machine-gun. The man in the right-hand position is the missile controller, who has a split-field monocular sight with magnification of ×1 and ×10 which can be traversed 55 degrees either side of the vehicle's centre line.

The five Swingfire missiles are carried in a launcher box on the hull roof, which is pivoted at the rear and elevated by an hydraulic ram. Five spare missiles are carried inside the vehicle but the launcher can only be reloaded from outside the hull. With a range in excess of 3,000 metres, the Swingfire can destroy main battle tanks. When launched, it is automatically programmed into the controller's field of view and then controlled on to the target by means of a joystick, the commands being conveyed to the missile through the wire it dispenses. The Striker is commonly used as a back-up vehicle by reconnaissance units equipped with light tanks and other light armoured vehicles.

A further member of the Scorpion family (not illustrated here) is the Samson Combat Vehicle, Recovery (FV 106). This uses the same hull as Spartan, is equipped with a heavy duty winch and twin spades on the hull rear, and is intended for the battlefield recovery of Scorpion tanks or other light armoured vehicles.

44 Combat, Vehicle, Reconnaissance, Full Tracked, Command, Sultan, and Combat Vehicle, Ambulance, Full Tracked, Samaritan, United Kingdom.

The armoured command and armoured ambulance derivatives of the Scorpion reconnaissance vehicle share a similar hull, rather like that of the Spartan armoured personnel carrier but increased in height to 2·016 metres to give greater headroom inside.

Sultan, the command vehicle, has an operating crew of three—driver, commander (who can also act as a radio operator) and radio operator, together with accommodation for two to three officers of armoured or mechanized units or formations. There is internal provision for map boards and documents and command radio sets. Extra batteries are carried for lengthy operation of the communications equipment. For use when the vehicle is stationary, a penthouse can be extended at the rear of the hull, to give approximately double the covered area. This item is normally carried, concertinaed, on the vehicle's back plate. One 7·62-mm. machine-gun is carried for the vehicle's protection, for which a pintle mount is provided.

The armoured ambulance, known as Samaritan, has accommodation in the hull for four stretchers, or two stretchers plus three sitting cases, or six sitting cases. The rear door (like that of the command vehicle) is larger than that of the personnel carrier, to make for easier handling of the stretchers. These can be slid into or out of the vehicle on movable racks attached to the inside of the hull walls. The Samaritan is, of course, unarmed. The vehicle commander (who would usually be a medical officer) for travelling has a position at the front right-hand side of the rear compartment, behind the engine, and is provided with a hatch containing five periscopes.

45 Carrier, Personnel, Full Tracked, FV 432, and Carrier, Maintenance, Full Tracked, FV 434, United Kingdom.

The full-tracked carrier in World War II was largely a British development in both its main forms—a specially designed series of open-topped light vehicles, epitomized by the Bren and Universal Carriers, used for a wide variety of roles on the one hand, and slightly modified tank or S.P. gun chassis, used principally as armoured personnel carriers on the other. Postwar development in Britain moved towards a vehicle combining features of both the early carriers and modified tanks. Experiments in the U.S.A. led to the requirement for a fully tracked and fully enclosed armoured vehicle to carry infantry accompanying armour, resulting in the M-75, M-59 and M-113 series, while parallel experiments in Britain with different models produced as prototypes or in relatively small numbers resulted in the FV 432 series.

The first prototypes of the FV 432 were ready for trials in 1961. Because long experiments had already been carried out with earlier vehicles having many features of the FV 432, it was possible for series production to be commenced in 1962 and the first standard vehicles were running by the following year.

Welded steel construction is used for the hull of the FV 432, making it heavier than the aluminium alloy American M-113 and also (unlike the M-113) making it unable to swim without special preparation. The engine is a Rolls-Royce six-cylinder two stroke multi-fuel engine, developing 240 h.p. and the suspension is of the torsion bar variety, carrying five medium-sized road-wheels each side. The track drive is at the front, as is also the engine (at the left side) and transmission, leaving a clear compartment at the rear of the vehicle. The driver is seated at the right, beside the engine, and the vehicle commander (who has a rotating cupola with three periscopes and opening hatch) is immediately behind him. The infantry section of ten men are seated, five each side, on benches hinged to the side walls of the rear compartment. Normal ingress and egress is through a large door in the rear plate, but there is also a large circular hatch in the roof from which the crew's personal weapons or, for example, a 81-mm. mortar can be operated.

The FV 432 has a maximum road speed of 52 km./hr and in water between 6 and 7 km./hr. For swimming, a flotation screen has to be erected round the top edge of the hull—a fairly quick process—and a trim board raised on the glacis plate. The latter is carried permanently on some vehicles but not on others.

As well as its basic role of carrying a section of riflemen, the FV 432 in its more-or-less standard form can carry an 81-mm. mortar; or a 120-mm. Wombat recoilless anti-tank gun (mounted in the roof); or a Carl Gustav anti-tank launcher. There are also command and ambulance (four stretcher) versions, externally similar to the armoured personnel carrier.

The Carrier, Maintenance, Full Tracked, FV 434 is basically the same mechanically as the FV 432 but is a specialized adaptation to meet the needs of the Royal Electrical and Mechanical Engineers for a vehicle capable of carrying out repair and maintenance of A.F.V.s in the field. It is equipped with a HIAB hydraulically operated crane, mounted on a turntable on the right-hand side of the hull roof. This crane can lift 3·05 tons on a short radius of 7–8 ft or 1·25 tons at around 12 ft. It can be used for changing the power plants of Chieftain tanks, or gun barrels. A full range of tools including a vice is carried, some of which are stored in a compartment at the rear of the vehicle: the cover of this folds down to form a bench. The layout of the stowage differed in the earlier models.

The FV 434 has a crew of four men (driver, commander and two fitters) and approximately the same performance (including amphibious capability) as the FV 432.

46 Launcher, Guided Missile, Carrier Mounted, Full Tracked, Swingfire, FV 438 and Carrier, FV 432 with Ranger, United Kingdom.

As well as its employment in various infantry roles and as a repair vehicle, already described, the FV 432 series has a number of uses with the Royal Artillery and Royal Engineers. One model carries the Field Artillery Computer Equipment (F.A.C.E.) for controlling field guns, and several variants of FV 432 are equipped with radar, including the Green Archer mortar locating radar system (FV 436, with the scanner mounted on the rear of the hull, which has a lowered roof) and the Cymbeline radar, which is replacing Green Archer. FV 432's are also used to carry ground surveillance radar and sonic detection equipment.

In addition to these passive functions, a version of the FV 432 is used as an anti-tank vehicle—the FV 438 armed with the Swingfire wire-guided rocket system. Two launchers are mounted on the hull roof near the rear. When the target is sighted in the periscopic sight, the missile is launched and then automatically programmed on to the target sight line, when the controller applies corrections to ensure a hit. The missile has a range of 4,000 metres. Fourteen are carried and can be loaded from the protection of the vehicle's armour.

The FV 432 is used by the Royal Engineers as a carrier for the Ranger anti-personnel mine-laying device. The small Ranger mines are carried in a rotatable framework mounted on the roof of the FV 432. The frame holds 72 tubes in three banks of twenty-four, each tube containing twenty mines. Ejection of the mines up to a range of 100 metres is by an electrically fired cartridge and the rate can be controlled to suit the speed of the vehicle and the density of mine coverage needed. The Ranger-equipped FV 432 can also tow the Bar Mine Layer, which is a trailer for laying the anti-tank Bar Mines. The Bar Mines are 27 in. (685 mm.) long and $4\frac{1}{4}$ in. (108 mm.) wide, and are made almost entirely of non-metallic materials and thus difficult to detect. In the laying process the Bar Mines are fed into a chute attached to the trailer after having their safety pins removed by a man sitting in the rear of the towing vehicle. A plough on the trailer cuts a furrow into which the Bar Mine is laid (after having been made active by a catch) and the furrow is then covered. Some 600–700 mines an hour can be laid in this way.

Minefield clearance can also be carried out by an FV 432 towing the Giant Viper trailer, which is described with the Combat Engineer Tractor.

47 Gun, Self-Propelled, 105-mm. Fd. Gun, Abbot and Falcon Self-Propelled A.A. Gun, United Kingdom.

The Abbot (a title continuing a Royal Artillery tradition of naming its S.P. guns after ecclesiastics) is the principal British Army field artillery weapon; towed guns of this calibre now being used only in specialized functions, such as for airborne operations.

Although of comparatively light calibre (and likely to be supplanted eventually by the joint British–German–Italian 155-mm. gun), the Abbot's 105-mm. gun is claimed to have a greater range (at 17,000 metres) than comparable weapons of other countries and a high explosive shell of greater lethality, with a rate of fire of twelve rounds per minute.

The chassis of the Abbot (or F.V. 433) has many components in common with the F.V. 432 series of armoured carriers, including a version of the Rolls-Royce six-cylinder two-stroke multi-fuel engine, developing 240 h.p. and associated transmission, and a similar suspension system of five medium-sized road-wheels each side, carried on torsion bars. Also, the location of the engine at the front left-hand side, with the driver at the right, leaving the rear of the hull clear is common to both S.P. gun and armoured personnel carrier.

The 105-mm. gun is mounted in a

fully rotating turret, with powered traverse, where it has a maximum elevation of 70 degrees and depression of 5 degrees. The other three crew members occupy the turret; the ammunition stowage (in turret and rear hull) consisting of 32–34 high explosive rounds and HESH rounds, for use against armour. A 7·62-mm. machine-gun can be mounted on the commander's cupola for the vehicle's defence.

A maximum road speed of 48 km./hr can be attained by the Abbot and the vehicle can be made amphibious by the erection of a screen normally carried, collapsed, round the top of the hull. Preparation takes about 13 minutes and the speed in water, propelled by the tracks, is 5 km/hr.

A version of the Abbot, built to the same engineering standards but stripped of all items not absolutely essential for the prime purpose of the vehicle, known as Value Engineered Abbot was designed primarily for the Indian Army between about 1965 and 1967 and subsequently approximately 100 were produced by Vickers Ltd for India. The most important differences from the standard Abbot are lack of the flotation screen; the engine modified for diesel fuel only; turret hand traverse instead of power traverse; simplified commander's cupola, non-rotating. Even the mesh guard over the exhaust pipe can be omitted to cut cost to the minimum in the Value Engineered Abbot; but, if required, modification of all features to bring the vehicle up to full British Army standard can be carried out subsequently. The alternative of a General Motors 214-h.p. diesel engine instead of the Rolls-Royce engine has been offered by the manufacturers.

The Falcon is a self-propelled anti-aircraft gun system for combating low flying aircraft and also light armoured vehicles, developed by Vickers Ltd and British Marco Ltd in conjunction with the Hispano-Suiza Group. It consists of a Value Engineered Abbot chassis on which is mounted a special turret containing two 30-mm. Hispano-Suiza automatic guns, with a rate of fire (each) of 650 rounds per minute. The guns are power traversed and elevated, and are stabilized against vehicle movement so can be fired, if necessary, on the move. In action, target information, visually acquired, is fed into a computer which provides data for bracketing the target.

The Falcon's system, unlike that of the French Oeil Noir, for instance, does not incorporate target acquisition and tracking radar because it is felt that low level air attack is not a serious threat in darkness or poor visibility. External field radar surveillance systems can, however, be used to give advance warning of the imminence of attack and its likely direction, so as to give the Falcon's crew with their optical fire control system a good chance of hitting the targets.

48 Tank, Bridge Layer, AVLB, Chieftain Mk. 5, United Kingdom.

The Chieftain Bridge Layer, or Armoured Vehicle Launched Bridge, as successor to the Centurion Bridge Layer used by the British Army, has again reverted to the 'scissors' type of bridge which was first introduced during World War II with Valentine and Covenanter tank bridge layers.

Claimed to be the longest tank-laid

bridge in service, the Chieftain's No. 8 Tank Bridge is 24·4 metres long and can span a gap of 22·8 metres wide and is class 60—that is to say, it will take A.F.V.s of up to 60 tons. In order to keep weight down so that the loaded bridge layer itself is within class 60, the bridge girders are made of high strength nickel-alloy steel, with decking and kerbs of aluminium alloy. When travelling, the bridge is carried folded over the Chieftain's hull, with the hinges at the rear. For launching, a hydraulic pump, driven by a power take-off from the tank's main engine, brings the bridge forward on to stabilizers, raising it to the vertical position, opening it out and then, when fully extended, placing it over the gap. The launching process takes between three and five minutes. Recovery of the bridge, which may be picked up from either end, using the reverse process, takes about ten minutes. Tracked vehicles cross the bridge using both track ways (each 1·62 metres wide, with a 0·76-metre gap between them), but small wheeled vehicles, such as Land-Rovers, can use a single trackway, thus making two-way traffic possible for such vehicles.

The Chieftain Bridge Layer is operated by a crew of three and weighs, complete with bridge, 53 tons.

49 Armoured Recovery Vehicle, Chieftain Mk. 5, and Armoured Recovery Vehicle, Beach, Centurion Mk. 5, United Kingdom.

The Chieftain Armoured Recovery Vehicle is intended to replace the similarly equipped Centurion A.R.V.

now that all Centurion main battle tanks have been superseded in the British Army by Chieftains.

Based on the Chieftain Mark 5, the armoured recovery vehicle version is turretless with a heightened hull roof, the commander's rotating cupola, mounting one remote-controlled 7·62-mm. machine-gun, occupying the highest point in the centre. The driver's position is at the left-hand side of the glacis plate and his seat lacks the reclining facility of the normal Chieftain battle tank. Besides commander and driver, the crew includes two fitters. Two winches are carried, the main one being of capstan type, driven mechanically by a power take-off from the tank's main engine. It has a maximum pull of 30 tons and has 120 metres of cable: as this is fed forward through a pulley on the glacis plate, control is easier than with the Centurion A.R.V.'s rear feed system. The secondary winch is of 3 tons capacity and has 300 metres of cable. It is hydraulically driven and is used for paying out the main winch cable and for light recovery duties. A range of pulley blocks is carried on the A.R.V. which can increase the purchase of the main winch to 90 tons when the bulldozer blade, mounted at the front of the A.R.V. and hydraulically operated, is used as an earth anchor.

The Chieftain A.R.V. can wade without preparation in water up to 1·07 metres deep and has a maximum speed of 42 km./hr. In the British Army, one A.R.V. is issued to each squadron of Chieftain main battle tanks. Chieftain A.R.V.s have been supplied to Iran.

The old Centurion continues in service in the British Army in a specialized version used for the recovery of vehicles and assisting landing craft in amphibious operations. A type of vehicle that has few parallels in other armies, the Centurion Beach Armoured Recovery vehicle is descended from British-operated Sherman tanks modified in 1943–44 particularly with the D-Day invasion in view. They did useful work in recovering 'drowned' vehicles and helping to keep the Normandy beaches clear.

The main features of the Centurion B.A.R.V. are the waterproofed engine, sealed hull and tall armoured superstructure, which enable it to work in water up to 2·896 metres deep. Not primarily intended for heavy recovery operations, the vehicle carries only a light winch at the front and a range of towing cables, but the crew of four includes a diver to enable some equipment to be fitted underwater. A rectangular box extending slightly in front of the tracks and faced with a rope fender is to enable the B.A.R.V. to push off and help refloat damaged or stranded landing craft.

50 Combat Engineer Tractor, Full Tracked, United Kingdom

The latest manifestation of the British Army's close interest in and development of armoured engineer (or pioneer) vehicles, the FV 180 Combat Engineer Tractor is a purpose-built vehicle intended to carry out most of the roles previously performed by the Centurion A.V.R.E. (Armoured Vehicle, Royal Engineers). The FV 180 is not, however, designed for the direct assault role and does not carry a mortar for attacking concrete fortifications: its tasks are

normally in the preparation of the ground for tanks and other fighting vehicles, and other battlefield tasks under fire.

By adopting a specially designed vehicle instead of an existing tank chassis, it has been possible to keep the Combat Engineer Tractor's weight down to 17·1 tons fully loaded, with consequent advantages in mobility and the possibility of giving the vehicle a good amphibious performance. Powered by a Rolls-Royce six-cylinder water-cooled diesel engine of 320 h.p., the FV 180 has a maximum road speed of 60 km./hr, and in water, propelled and manoeuvered by twin Hydrojets, 9 km./hr. To aid it in surmounting exceptionally steep slopes, or to help it emerge from water up a soft earth bank, an earth anchor or grapnel is carried which can be fired by a rocket, carrying a winch cable. The vehicle can then help itself along by means of its winch.

The hull of the Combat Engineer Tractor is of aluminium alloy, helping to keep the weight down. The suspension consists of five road-wheels each side (the rear one acting as an idler) sprung on torsion bars. Internally, the layout consists of the engine near the rear at the right-hand side, with the crew of two seated in tandem on the left at the highest point of the hull, under a superstructure with ten vision blocks all round. Each man has a separate hatch. This high position for the crew both improves observation and makes them less vulnerable to mine explosion. The crew seats can be revolved for different operations. For normal running the front man drives, but the second man has full duplicate controls: there are four reverse as well as four forward gears and land performance is nominally the same in both directions. The gear-box is in front of the engine, with the hydraulic pump for winch and shovel located above it, and the final drive and steering units are at the front of the vehicle. The winch cable outlet is on the long-sloping front glacis plate which also carries a large trim board for swimming, folded back when not in use.

The bulldozer equipment is attached to the back of the vehicle: the shovel is made of aluminium alloy with steel teeth and has a capacity of 1·7 cubic metres. A small jib, for handling engineer stores, with a lift of 4 tons, can be attached to the shovel, which also performs a function when the Combat Engineer Tractor is swimming. A load of expanded polyurethane is lashed to the shovel and helps to keep the vehicle trimmed while in the water. At the same time, flotation bags, kept under the trim board, are inflated when the trim board is erected: these help to keep the FV 180's nose up when entering the water. The hydro jet outlets are just above track level at either side of the bulldozer hydraulic arms.

The Combat Engineer Tractor is unarmed but it has smoke-bomb launchers for its own protection. It can perform a wide range of duties, including the following: earth moving, clearing obstacles, preparation of river crossings, making gun emplacements, etc.; assisting in bridging operations, by moving pontoons in water, etc.; helping to recover bogged-down vehicles; laying portable carpets or roadways (carried rolled up in the bulldozer shovel); towing trailers carrying supplies; and minefield clearance. In the last opera-

tion, the vehicle tows the Giant Viper equipment in its two-wheeled trailer. (The FV 180's towing bar is at the front, so it normally operates 'backwards' when towing.) The Giant Viper consists of a hose filled with explosive, which is propelled by a rocket across the minefield and exploded, detonating a clear lane.

51 **Remote Handling Equipment (Tracked) (EOD), Wheelbarrow Mk. 7,** United Kingdom.

The development of a remote-controlled machine to help deal with terrorist devices being tackled by the British Army in Northern Ireland was begun in 1971. The idea was to produce a robot vehicle that could undertake work previously carried out in person by explosives ordnance disposal personnel and so cut down the risks involved.

Three different organizations produced prototypes, of which the one called 'Wheelbarrow' was judged the best. The three-wheeled chassis of this device was adapted from an existing model of powered wheelbarrow, hence its name.

The first production Wheelbarrow Mark I arrived in Northern Ireland in April 1972 and co-operation between the Army and the designers enabled improvements, in the light of practical experience in operation, to be made. The Mark 2 had a power-steering system instead of the lanyard-operated tiller system of the Mark I and Mark 3 was four-wheeled and had skid-steering.

Wheelbarrow Mark 4 was a tracked version of Mark 3: the tracks gave it more of a 'go-anywhere' performance, enabling it to climb steps or kerbs in urban areas, for instance. By 1973 the Mark 5 had appeared: this had a 24-volt electrical system, the driving wheels were relocated to reduce slippage, and a closed-circuit television monitoring system (first used in Mark 3) was adopted as standard. The Mark 6 had a new pattern of boom, operated by two 12-volt motor actuators, with a reach both higher and lower than earlier models and was fitted with a panning facility on its closed-circuit television system.

The latest version of Wheelbarrow, Mark 7, differs from Mark 6 in having geared rather than chain drive, with infinitely variable speed control, and a mechanical grab in place of the previous scissors grapnel attachment.

The Wheelbarrow Mark 7 is only 1·22 metres long (excluding attachments) and weighs 195 kg. Its reversible electric motors, powered by two 12-volt batteries, give it an infinite range of speeds up to 33·5 metres per minute, with an endurance of two hours. The operating range with the standard cable and drum is 100 metres. The range of equipment it can carry and the tasks it can perform are as follows: three types of boom, for holding and positioning the various accessories, at heights ranging from ground level up to about 2·5 metres; a panning-head television camera, for investigating suspicious objects, with a 9-in. (228-mm.) monitoring screen; a window-breaking device, which can be used in conjunction with a small disruptive charge (for dealing with a car loaded with explosives, for example); a grab for removing containers suspected of containing

lethal devices; a car-towing hook, which can be placed by the Wheelbarrow, enabling a suspect car to be towed away (by means of a long tow rope) for subsequent investigation in a safe area; an automatic shot gun, holding five rounds, for destroying suspicious objects, for example, or for breaking door locks to force entry into buildings; and twin nail guns (mounted between the front 'horns' of the vehicle) to drive spikes into the floor when the Wheelbarrow enters buildings, to prevent the doors from closing and preventing easy retreat.

Manufactured by Morfax Ltd, the Wheelbarrow Mark 7 and its predecessors was developed by this company in conjunction with the British Ministry of Defence.

52 Tank, Combat, Full-Tracked, XM-1 (General Abrams), U.S.A.

Although the United States Army's efforts to develop a successor to the M-60 series have been costly, it is expected that the end result will be a main battle tank that will be substantially less expensive to maintain than its predecessors.

Following the abortive MBT-70 joint project with the German Federal Republic, new requirements were formulated in 1972 and contracts for prototypes were issued in June of the following year to the Defense Division of Chrysler Corporation and the Detroit Allison Division of General Motors Corporation. A considerable degree of latitude was allowed to the contractors in their designs.

Both Chrysler and General Motors delivered their prototypes to the Army for testing in February 1976. The possibility of standardizing components between the American tank and the German Leopard was also taken into consideration and the decision was taken to develop a turret for the XM-1 that would be capable of taking either the U.S. 105-mm. gun (originally of British design and common to many NATO countries) with a new, more effective, round, or a 120-mm. gun—the calibre favoured by the Germans.

The Chrysler project was chosen in November 1976 and Chrysler were awarded a Full Scale Engineering Development Contract for the construction of further prototypes and other development work, leading to full production of standard vehicles scheduled to commence in February 1980.

One of the principal factors leading to the choice of the Chrysler design was their use of the Avco Lycoming AGT-1500c gas turbine engine which, although somewhat less efficient than the diesel engine favoured by General Motors, and more expensive initially, it is claimed to be much more reliable and durable, with lower maintenance costs. The power output of 1,500 h.p. gives the Chrysler XM-1 the ability to accelerate from zero to 32 km./hr in 6·2 seconds and to reach a maximum of 70 km./hr. The engine is linked with an Allison automatic transmission and differential steering system.

The suspension consists of seven road-wheels each side, sprung on torsion bars—chosen instead of a hydropneumatic system because of

their lower vulnerability and simpler maintenance requirements. The leading torsion bars are specially protected against mine damage.

The main armament of the XM-1 is the 105-mm. gun with improved ammunition but provision has been made for adapting the turret to take either the German 120-mm. smooth bore gun or a British 120-mm. rifled gun. There is also a 7·62-mm. coaxial machine-gun, a 12·7-mm. machine-gun on the turret roof, for operation by the tank commander, and a 7·62-mm. machine-gun on a pintle mounting for the loader. Stabilization in elevation is provided for the 105-mm. gun and for the turret in the horizontal axis. The fire control unit also includes a thermal imaging night vision system.

The protection on the XM-1 is based on spaced armour and includes side-skirting plates over the upper half of the suspension. A crew of four operates the XM-1—commander, gunner and loader (all in the turret) and driver, who is in the front centre of the hull in a semi-reclining position.

The illustrations show a prototype Chrysler XM-1, armed with the 105-mm. gun.

53 Tank, Combat, Full Tracked, 105-mm. Gun, M-60A1, and Tank, Combat, Full Tracked, 152-mm. Gun, M-60A2, U.S.A.

The American M-48 medium tank first went into service with the U.S. Army in 1952 and, like its predecessors, the M-46 Pershing, of late World War II vintage, and M-47, was armed with a

90-mm. gun. The M-48 had many faults due, in the main, to lack of adequate tests and failure to rectify the weaknesses that did show up, before full-scale production began. Production variants corrected some of these design faults. The advent of the Soviet 100-mm. tank gun made it necessary for the M-48's gun to be replaced and the M-48E1, and the M-48A1E1 which followed it in production, was equipped with the British-designed 105-mm. gun.

A new tank was then planned to be armed from the start with the 105-mm. gun, although the first version, M-60, was merely a M-48 with suitable modifications.

Parallel to consideration of the British 105-mm. gun, a design for a 152-mm. gun-howitzer capable of firing both conventional (rifled) shot as well as fin-stabilized rocket missiles, controlled on to the target by means of radio micro-waves, was examined. Known as Shillelagh, this weapons system was intended for the main battle tank MBT-70 being jointly developed by the U.S.A. and Germany. The MBT-70 project in the end came to nothing but the Shillelagh system was installed in the M-551 light tank and, later, in a version of the M-60, the M-60A2. Considerable development difficulties occurred with the 152-mm. gun, not so much with the missile ammunition as with the conventional ammunition, which has a combustible cartridge case. Testing of the system on M-551s in action in Vietnam and further trials led to the solution of the problems, however.

All the M-60 series are powered by a Continental diesel twelve-cylinder engine of 750 h.p. situated at the rear, with an Allison transmission system driving rear track sprockets. The suspension is of the torsion bar variety and there are six medium-sized road-wheels and three track guide rollers each side. The cast hull contains the driver near the front in the centre and the commander, gunner and loader are in the turret, which like the hull is of cast construction.

The M-60 and M-60A1 both have a 105-mm. gun as main armament, accompanied by a coaxial 7·62-mm. machine-gun in the turret and a heavy 12·7-mm. machine-gun mounted in the commander's cupola on the turret roof. The main difference between these two models is that the M-60 has, as mentioned earlier, a modified M-48 hull.

The mounting in the M-60 of the Shillelagh system with its 152-mm. gun/launcher in a special turret has resulted in the M-60A2. Most of the performance characteristics, including the maximum speed of 48 km./hr, are unchanged despite the increase in loaded weight of around 3,000 kg. The quantity of ammunition carried is, however, reduced to forty-six rounds, compared with sixty-three rounds of 105 mm. for the M-60A1 and sixty for the M-60.

Only 526 M-60A2s were built and they are used to support conventional gun tanks, as their missiles have an effective range of over 3,000 metres, compared with the 105-mm. gun of M-60/M-60A1 which has an effective range of 1,800 metres using APDS ammunition. The M-60 and M-60A1 have been supplied to nearly a dozen armies, including that of the United

States, and production of the M-60A1, and an improved version the M-60A3, continues. The process of continually updating the M-48 and M-60 series has resulted in a confusing variety of hybrids and M-60A3 is the designation for the M-60A1 including a number of specified improvements, such as full stabilization for the main armament, a new laser range-finder, night vision equipment and an improved engine.

54 Armored Reconnaissance/Airborne Assault Vehicle, Full Tracked, 152 mm., M-551, U.S.A.

An air-portable light tank, the M-551, or General Sheridan, weighs just under 16 tons loaded and has the same main armament as the M-60A2 main battle tank. Development of the Sheridan (as the XM-551) began in early 1959 as a vehicle to replace both the M-41 Walker Bulldog light tank for reconnaissance and the M-56 self-propelled 90-cm. anti-tank gun as an airborne support vehicle.

The Shillelagh 152-cm. gun/launcher system is similar to that used in the M-60A2 and the now-abandoned MBT-70 main battle tank. Secondary armament consists of a 7·62-mm. machine-gun mounted in the turret coaxially with the main weapon and a 12·7-mm. machine-gun on the commander's cupola.

Lightness in weight is achieved by the use of an aluminium alloy forged hull and extensive use of aluminium in the engine, transmission and radiator. Weight has also been saved by attention

to detail in other components, such as hollow road-wheel arms used in the transverse torsion bar suspension system and aircraft-type cables for vehicle control linkages. The vehicle is amphibious—propelled in water by its tracks —by the use of a screen. The front of this screen is formed by a high surf board (with two see-through panels), which is normally carried folded on the front glacis plate, and the sides and back are of flexible fabric which is kept folded round the hull top when not in use. The side barriers are kept rigid when erected by means of support posts.

The M-551 is powered by a Detroit Diesel six-cylinder engine developing 300 h.p., which produces a maximum road speed of 70 km./hr and 5·6 km./hr in water.

A total of some 1,700 M-551s have been built and are in service only with the U.S. Army, which employs them for reconnaissance purposes in armoured units, including those in airborne formations. Some early production vehicles were used in action in Vietnam, as a result of which a number of faults were corrected and improvements made such as, for example, the addition of a shield to the machine-gun on top of the turret.

55 Carrier, Personnel, Full Tracked, Armored, M-113A1 Diesel, and Carrier, 107-mm. Mortar, Full Tracked, M-106A1, U.S.A.

The American M-113 Armored Personnel Carrier and its variants is one of the most widely used armoured vehicles in the world. Getting on for 70,000 have been built (including licensed production in Italy) and different versions of M-113 and M-113A1 are used by some thirty-six countries.

The first production vehicle to use aluminium armour, the M-113 was developed by the FMC Corporation from its earlier armoured personnel carrier, the M-59 which, together with the M-75, it eventually replaced. Although having the same carrying capacity (for ten infantrymen, plus vehicle crew) as the M-59 and M-75, the M-113 is some seven tons lighter in weight. It should be mentioned here that to offer the same degree of protection as steel armour, aluminium has to be approximately three times as thick. The thicker aluminium hull is, therefore, roughly the same weight but much more rigid than a steel hull of comparable protection. Overall weight savings in aluminium hull vehicles can be made by the elimination of many structural components).

The M-113 has a box hull with vertical sides, a steeply sloping glacis plate at the front and a ramp at the rear containing a single door. The infantry occupy longitudinal seats against each wall, five each side, facing inwards. A large circular three-piece hatch in the hull roof near the rear enables the men to use their personal weapons from the vehicle. The vehicle commander's position is roughly in the centre of the hull roof and is equipped with a 12·7-mm. machine-gun mounted on his revolving cupola. The driver is at the front left-hand side of the vehicle, next to the engine.

The engine on the M-113 is a Chrysler eight-cylinder petrol type,

developing 209 h.p. The M-113A1, which followed the M-113 in production in 1964 and, constitutes the bulk of vehicles produced, has instead a GMC six-cylinder diesel of 215 h.p. Transmission is to front sprockets, leaving the rear compartment entirely free of automotive components. The suspension of the M-113/M-113A1 consists of five road-wheels each side, carried on transverse torsion bars. Fully amphibious without preparation, other than erection of the trim vane carried on the glacis plate, the M-113 is propelled in water by its tracks, performance being enhanced by a rubber skirt covering the top run of the tracks. The maximum speed in water is just under 6 km./hr and on land about 68 km./hr.

There are many variants of the M-113 and M-113A1, one of which is the M-106A1 mortar carrier. This vehicle is mechanically identical to the M-113A1 and differs in other respects mainly in that the rear compartment has been modified so that the 4·2-in. (107-cm.) mortar mounted on a turntable can be fired through the roof hatch. A base-plate and bipod for the mortar when used outside the vehicle are carried on the side of the hull. This variant of the M-113A1 has a crew of six. A similar vehicle used by the Swiss Army is equipped with a 120-mm. mortar, and Rheinstahl in Germany have modified standard M-113A1s for use as 120-mm. mortar carriers. The M-125A1 has an 81-mm. mortar.

Some other variants of the M-113 series are described elsewhere in the U.S.A. section of this book and the Fire Support Vehicle based on the M-113A1 developed in Australia is dealt with under that country.

56 Carrier, Command Post, Full Tracked, M-577A1 and Carrier, M-113 with Radar, U.S.A.

Among the many variants of the M-113A1 Armored Personnel Carrier are command and radar vehicles. Many M-113s are used at battalion level and below only slightly modified as command vehicles but the M-577A1 has a special hull structurally adapted for its function. The height of the hull just behind the engine and driver in the M-577A1 has been raised by 0·64 metres to allow full standing height for the command staff in the rear compartment. Further space can be provided, when immobile, by the erection of a tent extension at the rear. Equipment includes between three and five radios for rear and forward links to headquarters and formations or units in the field and a 28-volt generator to operate them for long periods. Field telephone and fire direction control equipment is also carried.

The M-113 has been adapted as a carrier for various forms of radar equipment. This includes the Franco-German RATAC on German M-113s (Radarpanzer 2) and the British Green Archer mortar locating radar on German (Radarpanzer 3) as shown in the illustration, and Danish M-113s. The Green Archer radar can track a mortar bomb in flight and by means of a computer plot the location of the mortar itself. When adapted to carry Green Archer, the M-113 has the upper part of the rear of the hull cut away for the installation of the scanner on its turntable. Power is provided by a silent-running generator, suitable for use in forward areas.

57 Command and Reconnaissance Vehicle (Lynx), and Carrier, Command and Reconnaissance, Armored, M-114A1, U.S.A.

The M-113 was used as the starting point for the design of two different smaller vehicles produced, respectively, for the U.S. Army and as a private venture by the FMC Corporation. As both vehicles are intended for command as well as reconnaissance functions, they have relatively roomy aluminium hulls, although both normally operate with a crew of three (optionally four in the case of the M-114A1). One advantage of the resultant volume: weight ratio is that both vehicles are amphibious without special aids other than a trim vane carried at the front.

The first prototype of the FMC Corporation's project was completed in 1963, and although rejected by the U.S. Army was purchased by the Dutch Army (who received them from 1966 onwards to a total of 260) and the Canadian Army, supplied with 174, who have given it the name Lynx. Very much like a scaled-down M-113, with only four road-wheels each side, the internal layout differs from the M-113 in that the engine is at the rear, although the drive is still to sprockets at the front of the track. The engine is a Detroit Diesel, developing 215 h.p., similar to that of the M-113A1, so the $8\frac{1}{2}$ ton vehicle has a high maximum speed of 71 km./hr.

Both Dutch and Canadian vehicles were originally armed with a 12·7-mm. heavy machine-gun mounted externally on a cupola on the hull roof and capable of being fired from within the vehicle. There is also a pintle mounting near the rear roof hatch for a 7·62-mm. machine-gun. The Dutch vehicles, however, are being converted to take Oerlikon turrets mounting 25-mm. cannon in place of the cupolas with 12·7-mm. machine-guns. One of these modified Dutch vehicles is shown in the illustration.

The M-114, developed by the Cadillac Division of the General Motors Corporation also has four road-wheels each side, but has an internal mechanical layout more closely akin to the FMC Corporation's M-113 in that both engine and drive to the tracks are at the front. The engine is a Chevrolet V-8 cylinder petrol type, developing 160 h.p. and giving a maximum road speed of 58 km./hr. All versions of the M-114 have a 7·62-mm. machine-gun with two alternative mountings but the main armament has varied. In the M-114 this is a 12·7-mm. machine-gun on a pintle mounting on the hull roof, operated by the commander. The M-114A1 has provision for the weapon to be operated from inside the vehicle, and a later version is equipped instead with a 25-mm. Hispano-Suiza cannon.

Over 3,700 M-114s and M-114A1s have been built. Some were employed in Vietnam, where their cross-country performance in the terrain there was not satisfactory, but numbers are still in service with the U.S. Army.

58 **Landing Vehicle, Tracked— Personnel 7 and Landing Vehicle, Tracked—Engineer 7**, U.S.A.

The United States has been in the fore-front in the development of amphibious personnel and cargo carriers since World War II and Landing Vehicles Tracked from this period are still in service with some armies. The LVT-P5 (personnel carrier), and the mechanically similar LVT-H5 (with 105-mm. howitzer), and specialized variants, developed from 1950, in service from 1951 and produced up to 1957, have now been replaced by the LVTP-7 series.

Designed by the FMC Corporation in 1966, the fifteen prototypes of the experimental model, known as LVTPX-12, were completed between 1967 and 1969. The vehicle in its final form, known as LVTP-7, was running in 1970.

The LVTP-7 has a fully enclosed hull with an upturned nose plate or bow of an unusual angular design, found by experiment to reduce water resistance and turbulence. The suspension consists of six road-wheels each side, carried on transverse torsion bars. The engine and transmission are located at the front and the drive sprockets are at the front of the track. A power take-off unit supplies engine power to water jets in the rear of the hull, just over the track idler wheels, for propulsion in water. The jet outlets are fitted with movable deflectors for steering and reversing. The engine is a Detroit Diesel of eight cylinders, developing 400 h.p. This produces a maximum speed on land of 63 km./hr and $13\frac{1}{2}$ km./hr on water. An interesting point is that both tracks and waterjets can be driven simultaneously—a useful feature when travelling in shallow water or when leaving the water, for example.

The LVTP-7 can carry twenty-five infantrymen, seated in three longitudinal rows, in addition to the crew. The latter consists of three men—the driver, who sits near the front at the left, the commander, just behind the driver, and the gunner, who occupies a turret, armed with one 12·7-mm. machine-gun, on the right-hand side of the hull roof. There is a large square ramp at the rear for loading cargo and this contains a door for the infantry.

The other members of the LVTP-7 family include the LVTC-7 command vehicle; the LVTR-7 recovery vehicle; and the LVTE-7. The latter, Landing Vehicle, Tracked, Engineer, Mark 7, is designed primarily for mine clearance in amphibious operations. For this purpose, a triple rocket launcher is carried in the rear compartment. For employment, the hull roof doors are opened, the launcher raised, and the three rockets are fired in succession over the minefield. The rockets carry line charges which are exploded, detonating the mines. To help level a path through the cleared minefield, and for other engineering tasks, a hydraulically oper-ated bulldozer blade is mounted at the front of the vehicle. The LVTE-7 has a crew of six men—three, as for the LVTP-7, and three to operate the rocket launcher.

About 1,000 vehicles of the LVTP-7 series have been delivered to the United States Marine Corps, where they have replaced earlier L.V.T.s. Some LVTP-7s have also been supplied to other countries.

59 Gun, Field Artillery, Self-Pro-pelled, 175-mm., M-107, and How-itzer, Heavy, Self-Propelled, 8 in., M-110, U.S.A.

In 1956 the United States felt the need for a fresh range of artillery weapons that would be air portable, and also the desire to achieve a much greater com-monality of components over the whole field of light armoured vehicles. The advent of the promising T-113 alu-minium hull armoured personnel car-rier (prototype of the M-113 series) at this time led to components of the armoured personnel carrier being used for the family of S.P. guns that was developed. Two successful vehicles to emerge were the T-235 175-mm. S.P. gun, which eventually became the M-107, and the T-236 8-in. S.P. howitzer, which after modifications became the M-110.

Designed by the Pacific Car and Foundry Company, the M-107 and M-110 have identical chassis and even the gun mountings are similar. The suspension is like a shortened version of the M-113s, without a separate idler wheel, the rear road-wheel, in contact with the ground, performing this function. The driver, who sits at the front left-hand side of the hull, is the only member of the crew to be protected, seats for the other four crew members travelling on the vehicle being provided around the gun mount-ing. Eight further crew members travel in a supporting vehicle (usually an M-548 cargo carrier), which also carries ammunition. The engine, located at the front right-hand side of the hull, is an eight-cylinder Detroit Diesel of 405 h.p. This produces, in both M-107 and M-110, a maximum speed of 56 km./hr, although the overall perform-ance of the M-107, which is getting on for 2 tons heavier than M-110, is probably slightly inferior to the M-110s. The M-107/M-110 have no pro-vision for amphibious operations.

The artillery piece on the M-107 is the 175-mm. model M-113, 60 calibres long. This gun fires an H.E. shell weighing 66·6 kg. to a maximum range of 32 km. The M-110's weapon is the 8-in. (203-mm.) model M2A1E1 howitzer with a calibre length of 25. This has a maximum range of 17 km. and the H.E. shell weighs 90·7 kg.

A dozen different countries, including the U.S.A., use the M-107 or M-110, or both. The illustrations show an Italian-used M-107 and a British M-110.

A replacement for both the M-107 and M-110, known as M110E2, is under development. This will use existing chassis and mountings (with modifications), the 175-mm. and 203-mm. barrels being replaced by a new and much longer 203-mm. barrel. The new gun should have a range somewhere between those of the two present guns.

60 Howitzer, Medium, Self-Propelled, 155-mm. M-109G, and Lance Guided Missile System, U.S.A.

Two tactical field artillery systems currently in service with the U.S. Army, and others, are the M-109, which is a conventional self-propelled howitzer, and the Lance, a surface-to-surface guided missile.

The M-109 was developed at around the same time as the M-107 and M-110, but because of its lighter and smaller calibre gun offers full armour protection for the crew within the same, air-portable, weight and can also be provided with nuclear, biological and chemical warfare protection and can be made to swim.

Sharing a common chassis with the 105-mm. S.P. M-108, both vehicles use the same engine as the M-107 and M-110—the 405-h.p. eight-cylinder Detroit Diesel. This gives the M-109 a top speed of 56 km./hr. On water, propelled by its tracks and made amphibious by the addition of nine air bags attached to the sides and front of the hull, the speed is about 6½ km./hr.

The suspension of the M-109 consists of seven road-wheels each side, carried on transverse torsion bars. The drive sprockets are at the front and the engine is in the front right-hand side of the hull, with the driver beside it at the left. The rear half of the hull consists of the fighting compartment, surmounted by the large fully enclosed rotating turret, in which is mounted the M-126 155-mm. howitzer, with a length of 23 calibres. The weapon has a maximum elevation of 75 degrees and maximum range, with a 43·5 kg. H.E. round, of 14·7 km.

An improved model, known as M-109G, uses a Rheinmetall-designed weapon with several improvements, having a range of 18·5 km. The vehicles only are supplied from the U.S.A. and the guns are installed in Germany for the Bundeswehr, or in Italy (by OTO Melara) for the Italian Army. There are also longer barrelled (39 calibres) versions of the M-109, the M-109A1 with a range of 18 km. which is already in service, and an improved model of the Rheinmetall gun under development by OTO Melara with a range of 24 km. Some fifteen countries use M-109 in different versions. Those used by the Swiss Army (M-109U) have been modified in Switzerland to take a semi-automatic loader and have a rate of fire of six rounds per minute—double that of the standard M-109. A M-109G in Italian use is shown in the illustration.

The Lance tactical guided missile system is now in service with several countries. Development was commenced in 1962 as a replacement for the Honest John unguided rocket then used by leading NATO countries. Later, work was concentrated on an extended range Lance which could replace the Sergeant guided missile. The first flight test of the Extended Range Lance took place in 1969 and it was classified by the U.S. Army as Standard A when fitted with a nuclear warhead in May 1972.

The complete Lance system consists of the missile, two types of launcher and ancillary equipment. Two tracked carrier vehicles are usually employed— the self-propelled launcher vehicle (M-752) and the loader–transporter vehicle (M-688). Both are derivatives of the M-548 unarmoured cargo carrier. The Lance can be launched from the M-752 or from a two-wheeled 'zero length launcher', which can be towed by a truck if necessary. All the equipment is air-transportable.

The loader–transporter vehicle M-688 can carry two missiles and is equipped with an hydraulic crane for transferring them to the launcher, the tracked M-752 normally being used as the firing platform.

All launch functions for Lance are controlled by a monitor/programmer, consisting of a combined analog and digital computer. The missile is propelled by a single-stage pre-packaged liquid fuel rocket over a range of about 112 km. with a nuclear warhead of 210 kg. The new neutron missile can also be launched by Lance. Other, non-nuclear, warheads of around 450 kg. can, for example, disperse guided sub-missiles to seek and track enemy armour. A new version of Lance, Lance 2, uses a solid propellant fuel rocket.

61 Gun, Anti-Aircraft Artillery, Self-Propelled, 20-mm., M-163, and Guided Missile System Intercept— Aerial, Carrier Mounted (Chaparral), U.S.A.

The Vulcan and Chaparral equipments together make up a low level anti-aircraft system. Vulcan consists of a 20-mm. revolving multi-barrel gun mounted in a turret on the hull of a modified M-113A1 armoured personnel carrier. Equipped with range-finding radar, but aimed visually and fired when an electronic indicator tells the gunner that the target is within range, the six barrels of the Vulcan can achieve a total rate of 3,000 rounds per minute. A lower rate of 1,000 rounds per minute is also available for use against ground targets. Nineteen hundred rounds of ammunition are carried, including tracer, incendiary, armour-piercing and high explosive.

The Chaparral consists of four modified Sidewinder heat-seeking missiles mounted on a turntable launcher on the rear of the hull of a modified M-548 tracked cargo carrier. The missiles are optically sighted but the final phase of their flight on to the target is controlled by signals from their passive infra-red target-seeking heads. The missiles weigh about 84 kg. each and eight are carried in reserve on the vehicle as well as the four on the launcher.

Vulcan and Chaparral are the U.S. Army's current air defence against low-flying subsonic and supersonic aircraft. Both systems have also been supplied to Israel.

62 Recovery Vehicle, Full Tracked, Medium, M-88, and Recovery Vehicle, Full Tracked, Light, Armored, M-578, U.S.A.

These two armoured recovery vehicles are intended for the battlefield recovery of tanks and other armoured vehicles up to about 56,000 kg. (M-88) or 30,000 kg. (M-578) respectively.

The medium recovery vehicle uses many components of the M-48 tank series, including the twelve-cylinder Continental petrol engine and generally similar running gear, but has a specially designed hull. The suspension, like that of the M-48, is of the torsion bar type and has six road-wheels each side, but the track base is longer and the upper run of the track is lower than that of the medium tank. The equipment includes a non-rotating A-frame jib, pivoted near the front of the hull and having a maximum lift of 25,400 kg.; a main winch with a pull of 40,800 kg., for which 61 metres of cable is carried; and a secondary (hoist) winch with a capacity of 22,680 kg. A hydraulically operated bulldozer blade is mounted at the front of the vehicle and this is used as a stabilizer for the jib as well as for earth moving. A more unusual facility for an armoured recovery vehicle is an auxiliary fuel pump, which enables the M-88 to transfer fuel to other armoured vehicles.

About 1,000 M-88s have been built

and they are in service with several armies equipped with American tanks, besides the U.S. Army. It is likely that many of these will eventually be rebuilt to the same chassis mechanical standards as the M-60 tank series, including the substitution of a diesel for the petrol engine.

The light recovery vehicle M-578 uses the chassis of the self-propelled guns M-107 and M-110, which have a layout conducive to the installation at the rear of a fully revolving crane in an armoured turret. This crane has a maximum capacity of 13,620 kg.—to the rear only, when the stabilizing spade at the back is in position. The vehicle is operated by a crew of three —the driver at the front left-hand side, alongside the engine, and the other two men in the crane turret. One 12·7-mm. heavy machine-gun is carried for defence, pintle-mounted on the turret roof.

Design of the M-578 commenced (as the T-120) in 1957 and the first production vehicle was completed in 1962. The production line continues and vehicles have been supplied to eight countries (including the U.S.A.) using American M-107 and M-110 S.P. guns and other light armoured vehicles.

63 Combat Engineer Vehicle, Full Tracked, M-728, and Armored Vehicle Launched Bridge, U.S.A./ Italy.

The chassis of the M-60, as the current United States medium tank, has been used as the basis of a family of support vehicles having the advantage of roughly the same performance as well as many components in common. Two of the most important of these derivatives are an armoured engineer vehicle and a tank bridge layer.

The Combat Engineer Vehicle, M-728, is intended for a variety of engineering tasks in or near the battlefield, such as the destruction of concrete fortifications, the levelling or filling of earthwork defences and the preparation of positions for artillery or dug-in tanks. The basic chassis is that of the M-60A1, complete with turret including the commander's cupola with its machine-gun. The main armament is, however, a short-barrelled 165-mm. gun firing a 30-kg. demolition charge with a range of 1,000 metres, capable of destroying concrete emplacements. A coaxial machine-gun is also mounted in the turret.

A secondary function of the turret is to act as a turntable for an A-frame jib. This crane, which has a 15-ton lift, is pivoted near the front of the turret and is carried over the rear deck of the tank when not in use. The turret also has a two-speed winch mounted on the rear. For earth-moving tasks, an hydraulically operated bulldozer blaze is carried at the front of the vehicle's hull.

The development of the M-728 began with the T-118 experimental vehicle, using a T-95 tank chassis. This was followed by the T-118E1 and then the T-118E2 on the M-60A1 chassis, which was standardized as the M-728 by the time it entered production in 1965.

The M-60 A.V.L.B. (Armoured Vehicle Launched Bridge) consists of a scissors-type bridge mounted on a turretless M-60 tank chassis. The bridge itself is the same as that previously fitted on M-48 chassis. It is of aluminium alloy construction and is hydraulically operated. Opened out, it is 63 ft (19·202 metres) long and can bridge a gap of 60 ft (18·288 metres). Pivoted at the front of the vehicle, the bridge can be laid in three minutes and retrieved in a minimum of ten minutes. A new lightweight bridge for the M-60 chassis with a span of 95 ft (28·956 metres) for a gap of 90 ft (27·432 metres) is in the course of development.

The Italian company Astra SpA has designed an interesting armoured vehicle launched bridge which can be used with American M-47 (as shown in the illustration), M-48 or M-60 tank chassis, or (as employed by the Israeli Army) the British Centurion chassis. A scissors bridge of mixed steel and aluminium alloy construction, the A-26 is 22 metres long when extended and can carry up to 54 tons. The end ramps can be adjusted vertically downwards to form supports, enabling a second bridge to be launched from the first, to give a clear span with two bridges of between 36 and 38 metres. The launching mechanism is hydraulic, and the bridge can be recovered from either end. A time of six minutes is claimed for either launching or recovery of the bridge.

64 Infantry Combat Vehicle, M-980, Yugoslavia.

Not long after World War II, a Yugoslavian version of the Soviet T-34/85 tank appeared with a turret apparently made locally. The bulk of the A.F.V.s used by Yugoslavia until recently were, however, standard equipment of American or Soviet manufacture.

A new armoured personnel carrier entirely of Yugoslav design appeared in public for the first time in 1965. This vehicle, known as M-60 or M-590 is rather high and bulky and with a diesel engine of only 140 h.p. has a relatively low performance. It was succeeded in 1975 by a much more advanced vehicle, the M-980, fully equipped as an infantry combat vehicle. This has a well shaped hull with a long sloping glacis plate. The driver is at the front left-hand side, with the engine beside him at the right. The engine is a Hispano-Suiza/SNECMA eight-cylinder diesel of 280 h.p., as fitted in the French AMX-10P. The rear compartment has accommodation for six to eight infantrymen with their personal weapons, for the operation of which eight ports in the hull sides and rear are provided. The other two crew members are the commander and gunner.

The M-980 is particularly well armed for a M.I.C.V. The centrally located turret contains a 20-mm. Hispano-Suiza cannon and two 7·92-mm. machine-guns and a twin launcher for 'Sagger' (NATO name) SS anti-tank missiles.

The vehicle is amphibious, with a maximum water speed of 8 km./hr. On roads 70 km./hr can be attained.

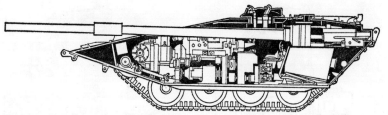

Stridsvagn Strv. 103—length (excluding gun) 7·0 metres (8·4 metres with stowage bins).

Bergepanzer 2, Leopard—length 7·57 metres.

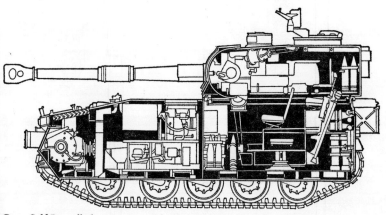

Gun, Self-Propelled, 105 mm. Fd. Gun, Abbot—length (excluding gun) 5·709 metres.

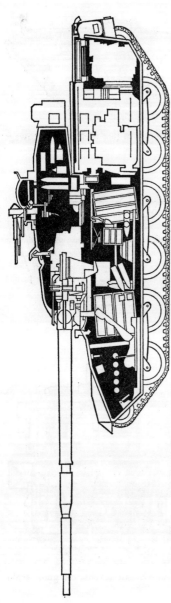

Tank, Combat, 120 mm. Gun, Chieftain Mk. 3—length (excluding gun) 7·52 metres.

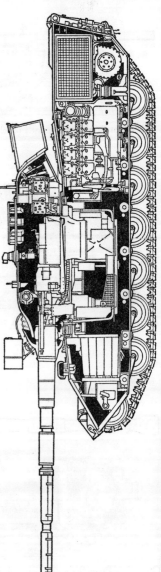

Kampfpanzer Leopard 1—length (excluding gun) 7·09 metres.

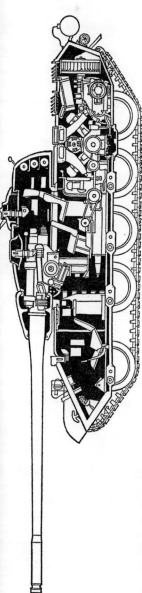

T-54A (Main Battle Tank)—length (excluding gun) 7·09 metres.

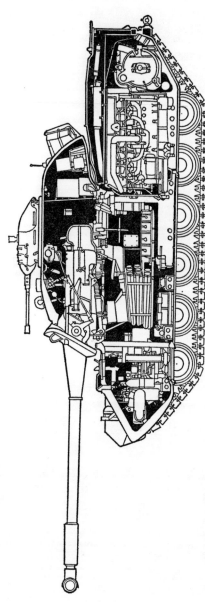

Tank, Combat; Full Tracked, 90 mm. Gun, M-48A2—length (excluding gun) 6·87 metres.

APPENDIX

Armoured Fighting Vehicle Camouflage Colours

The notes which follow give some guidance on the A.F.V. camouflage colours used by the countries—both of manufacturer and user—that are included in this book. It must be borne in mind, however, that to the eye the colour of a vehicle will differ widely with light and shade and that its paintwork will be changed in appearance, often quite drastically, by ageing, wear, or such additions as dust or mud.

Where one colour only is quoted, this is believed to be normal, but in any country at any time other schemes may be used to meet specific circumstances.

All NATO vehicles commonly show (at the front) the standard bridge group sign of a black figure on a yellow disc.

Argentina

Overall olive green, sometimes with other colours to make a disruptive pattern.

Australia

Overall olive drab colour. British-type tactical markings are used.

Austria

Overall dark green, similar to NATO green but with less of an olive shade. The National sign of a white hollow inverted triangle within a white ring is carried on A.F.V.s.

Belgium

Overall olive drab. Vehicle registration numbers are in black, preceded by a small rectangle in the national colours, on a white plate. Formation and tactical signs are usually carried.

Chinese Peoples Republic

Dark to medium green, overall. The national sign of a red star, outlined in yellow, is sometimes carried on A.F.V.s.

Czechoslovakia

Olive green overall. The national sign of a disc in blue, red and white segments is generally carried on A.F.V.s.

France

Olive drab colour overall. A tiny national tricolour flag precedes the vehicle number at the front and rear of the hull of A.F.V.s. Various regimental signs are used.

German Federal Republic (West Germany)

Normally, overall dark greyish-green, although sometimes a two- or three-colour disruptive scheme is used. The national marking is a black Iron Cross, outlined in white. Tactical numbers in white, or white outline, are commonly used on A.F.V.s, also, sometimes, small signs indicating the type of unit etc. The vehicle registration number in black, with prefix 'Y' and a small black/red/yellow sign (the national flag) is carried at front and rear on a white rectangle.

German Democratic Republic (East Germany)

Overall grey or olive green, with the D.D.R. national sign in black, yellow, red and gold in a small circle.

Holland

Overall olive green. Vehicle registration numbers are in black, prefixed by 'KN' or 'KZ' on a yellow rectangular plate, carried at front and rear of A.F.V.s.

India

Dark green overall. Disruptive pattern added sometimes. British-type tactical markings are used.

Israel

Overall yellowish sand colour. Vehicle registration numbers are in white on a black rectangle. Tactical signs (usually Hebrew characters in white) sometimes used. Also unit signs, mostly in white but sometimes using other colours.

Italy

Olive green overall. National sign (green/white/red rectangle) carried at front and rear. Vehicle number is in black, prefixed by 'EI' in red, on white rectangle.

Japan

Olive green overall. A multi-coloured disruptive pattern sometimes used. National sign—red disc sun on white rectangle is usually shown on A.F.V.s.

Poland

Olive green overall. National sign (diamond, quartered in red and white) carried on most A.F.V.s. Large white tactical numbers often used. Some unit or formation signs also appear sometimes.

Soviet Union

Overall dark olive green. Airborne forces have white parachute sign. Large white tactical numbers usually carried on tanks and armoured personnel carriers. The Red Star national sign appears, normally, to be used only on formal parades.

Sweden

A four colour scheme, using dark green, light green, light brown and black in a zig-zag pattern is to be applied to all A.F.V.s. Vehicle registration numbers are in yellow at front and rear.

Switzerland

Overall olive (brownish) drab colour. Vehicle numbers, prefixed by 'M' in white shown at front and rear of A.F.V.s White tactical signs—large numbers—used and (sometimes) unit insignia.

United Kingdom

Overall NATO green (dark olive green). Black disruptive patches added in Europe. In snow conditions, white is added, leaving some green. For desert conditions 'light stone' colour is used with black patches. Vehicle numbers (two digits, two letters, two digits, e.g. 13EA81) are in white at front and rear. Vehicle call signs are in white and follow a system such as 34=C Squadron (or 3rd fighting squadron), 4th Troop, Troop leader; 34A=2nd tank and so on. World War II tactical signs of a diamond for regimental (or battalion) H.Q., triangle—'A' Squadron; square—'B' Squadron; circle—'C' Squadron are often still used. Tanks and other A.F.V.s in B.A.O.R. only have a small national flag painted on front and rear.

U.S.A.

Olive drab or Forest Green overall, except where the four colour pattern scheme is used for tactical vehicles. The latter consists of four colours (including black) selected from a standard range of twelve colours. Typical combinations are (1) Sand (greyish, rather than yellow), Earth Red, Dark Green and Black, with the Sand and Earth Red predominating, Green and Black being used sparingly. This scheme has been used by the U.S. Army in West Germany. (2) Dark Green, Light Green, Earth Red and Black, with the two greens predominating and only small patches of the Earth Red and Black. This is suitable for wooded areas. The U.S. national sign used with the four colour schemes is a black five-pointed star and the U.S. Army vehicle number is also shown in black. Various geometric coloured tactical signs are sometimes used on armoured vehicles.

Yugoslavia

Greyish-green, overall. Tactical markings apparently not used.

Ref. No.	Type	Weight tons	Metres				Armament
			Length (hull)	Length (inc. gun)	Width	Height	
1	*Argentina:* TAM	29·5	6·775	8·23	3·25	2·42	1 105 mm., 1 7·62 m m.g. (co-ax), 1 7·62 (AA)
5	*Chinese P.R.:* T-59	40·6	6·45	9·0	3·27	2·4	1 100 mm., 1 7·62 m m.g. (co-ax), 1 7·62 (hull), 1 12·7 mm. (AA)
7	*France:* AMX-30	36	6·59	9·48	3·1	2·28	1 105 mm., 1 12·7 m m.g. (co-ax), 1 7·62 m.g. (AA)
13	*Germany:* Leopard I	40	7·09	9·54	3·25	2·62	1 105 mm., 1 7·62 m m.g. (co-ax), 1 7·62 (AA)
13	Leopard IA3	42·4	7·09	9·54	3·37	2·62	1 105 mm., 1 7·62 m m.g. (co-ax), 1 7·6: (AA)
19	*Japan:* Type 61	35	6·3	8·19	2·95	2·49	1 90 mm., 1 7·62 mm m.g. (co-ax), 1 12·7 m.g. (AA)
19	Type 74	38	6·85	9·09	3·18	2·48	1 105 mm., 1 7·62 m m.g. (co-ax), 1 12·7 m.g. (AA)
24	*Soviet Union:* T-55	36	6·45	9·0	3·27	2·4	1 100 mm., 1 7·62 m (co-ax)
25	T-62	36·5	6·715	9·77	3·35	2·4	1 115 mm., 1 7·62 m (co-ax), 1 12·7 mm (AA)
34	*Sweden:* Strv. 103B	39	8·4	9·8	3·6	2·5	1 105 mm., 2 7·62 m m.g. (hull), 1 7·62 m.g. (AA)
38	*Switzerland:* Pz61	38	6·78	9·43	3·06	2·72	1 105 mm., 1 20 mm (co-ax), 1 7·5 mm. (AA)
38	Pz68	39·7	6·9	9·49	3·14	2·74	1 105 mm., 1 7·5 mm (co-ax), 1 7·5 mm.
40	*United Kingdom:* Chieftain Mk 3	54·1	7·52	10·79	3·504	2·895	1 120 mm., 1 12·7 ranging m.g., 1 7·6 m.g. (co-ax), 1 7·62
40	Chieftain Mk 5	55	7·518	10·79	3·504	2·895	1 120 mm., 1 12·7 ranging m.g., 1 7·6 m.g. (co-ax), 1 7·6
39	Vickers M.B.T.	38·6	7·92	9·73	3·168	2·64	1 105 mm., 1 12·7 ranging m.g., 1 7·6 m.g. (co-ax), 1 7·6 (AA)
41	Centurion (Vickers retrofit)	52·0	7·823	9·85	3·39	3·00	1 105 mm., 1 7·62 m.g. (co-ax)
53	*U.S.A.:* M-60A1	49	6·946	9·31	3·631	3·257	1 105 mm., 1 7·62 m.g. (co-ax), 1 12· m.g.
53	M60A2	52	6·946	7·28	3·631	3·108	1 152 mm., 1 7·62 m.g. (co-ax), 1 12· m.g.
52	Xm-1	53·39	7·92	9·76	3·65	2·89	1 105 mm., 1 7·62 (co-ax), 1 12·7 mm 7·62 mm. (on turre

Engine	h.p.	Speed km./hr road	Speed km./hr water	Range km	Crew	Notes
...er Benz 6 cyl. ...l	710	75		600	4	
...12 cyl.	520	50		500	4	
...no-Suiza 12 cyl. ...l	720	65		650	4	
...er–Benz 10 cyl. ...l	830	65		600	4	
...er–Benz 10 cyl. ...l	830	65		600	4	
...bishi 12 cyl. ...l	600	45		200	4	
...bishi 10 cyl. ...l	750	53		500	4	
...V-55 12 cyl. ...diesel	580 700	50 50		500 500	4 4	
...Royce 6 cyl. ...plus ...ing gas turbine	240 490	50	6	390	3	
...er–Benz 8 cyl.	630	55		300	4	
...er–Benz 7 cyl.	660	60		300	4	
...d 12 cyl. multi-	750	48		500	4	
...d 12 cyl. multi-	750	48		500	4	
...d 12 cyl. multi-	650	56	6·5	480	4	
...l Motors 12 cyl.	715	40			4	
...ental 12 cyl.	750	48		500	4	
...ental 12 cyl.	750	48		500	4	
...Lycoming gas ...e	1500	70		450	4	With 120-mm. Rheinmetall gun: 54·42 ton, length inc. gun 9·80 m.

| Ref. No. | Type | Weight tons | metres | | | | Armament |
			Length	Length (inc. gun)	Width	Height	
	Austria:						
3	Panzerjäger	17·5	5·58	7·78	2·50	2·36	1 105 mm., 1 7·62 m m.g. (co-ax)
	France:						
8	AMX-13	15·0	4·88	6·36	2·51	2·23	1 105 mm., 1 7·62 m m.g. (co-ax)
8	AMX-13 (AA)	17·2	5·373		2·5	3·794	2 30 mm.
	Germany:						
15	Gepard	45·1	7·27	7·7	3·25	4·03	2 35 mm.
	Soviet Union:						
26	PT-76	14	6·91	7·63	3·14	2·25	1 76·2 mm., 1 7·62 m m.g. (co-ax)
28	ZSU-57-2	28·0	6·22	8·48	3·27	2·75	2 57 mm.
28	ZSU-23-4	14	6·3		2·95	2·25	4 23 mm.
	Sweden:						
35	Ikv-91	15·5	6·41	8·84	3·0	2·355	1 90 mm., 1 7·62 mm m.g. (co-ax)
	United Kingdom:						
42	Scorpion	7·96	4·338		2·184	2·096	1 76 mm., 1 7·62 mm (co-ax)
42	Scimitar	7·89	4·388	4·74	2·184	2·115	1 30 mm., 1 7·62 mm m.g. (co-ax)
47	Falcon	15·85	5·333		2·641	2·514	2 30 mm.
	U.S.A.:						
54	M-551	15·83	6·299		2·819	2·272	1 152 mm., 1 7·62 m m.g. (co-ax) 1 12·7

Engine	h.p.	Speed km./hr road	water	Range km.	Crew	Notes
er (Steyr) 6 cyl. el	300	67		520	3	
AM 8 cyl. petrol	250	60		350	3	
AM 8 cyl. petrol	250	60		300	3	Height includes radar.
10 cyl. diesel	840	65		600	3	Height includes radar.
el V-6 6 cyl. diesel	240	44	10	260	3	
el V-54 12 cyl .diesel	520	48		400	6	
el V-6 6 cyl. diesel	240	44		260	4	
o 6 cyl. diesel	295	64	7	550	4	
ar 6 cyl. petrol	195	81	6·5	644	3	
ar 6 cyl. petrol	195	81	6·5	644	3	
s-Royce 6 cyl. lti-fuel	240	48		390	3	
oit Diesel 6 cyl.	300	70	5·6	600	4	

Ref. No.	Type	Weight tons	metres			Armament
			Length	Width	Height	
2	*Australia:* M-113A1 FSV	26·3	4·86	2·68	2·87	1 76 mm., 1 7·62 mm. m.g. (1 m.g.
4	*Austria:* Schützenpanzer 4K4FA	12·5	5·40	2·50	1·65	1 12·7 mm. m.g.
5	APC	10·0				1 12·7 mm. m.g.
5	*Chinese P.R.:*					
6	*Czechoslovakia:* OT-62	15	7·08	3·14	2·038	1 7·62 mm. m.g.
9	*France:* AMX13VC1	14·0	5·544	2·51	1·92	1 7·62 mm. m.g. or 1 12·7 mr m.g. (co-ax)
9	AMX10P	13·8	5·778	2·78	2·54	1 20 mm., 1 7·62 mm. m.g. (c
14	*Germany:* Marder	28·2	6·79	3·24	2·86	1 20 mm., 1 7·62 mm. (co-ax) 1 7·62 mm. m.g.
20	*Japan:* Type 60	11·8	4·85	2·4	1·70	1 7·62 mm. m.g., 1 12·7 mm.
21	Type 60 (mortar)	12·0	4·85	2·4	1·7	1 107 mm. mortar, 1 12·7 mm
20	Type 73	14	5·6	2·8	1·7	1 7·62 mm. m.g., 1 12·7 mm.
27	*Soviet Union:* BMP-1	12·5	6·75	3·0	2·0	1 73 mm., 1 7·62 mm. m.g. (1 ATGW launcher
27	BMD	8·5	5·3	2·65	1·85	1 73 mm., 1 7·62 mm. m.g. (c 1 ATGW launcher
36	*Sweden:* Pbv 302	13·5	5·35	2·86	2·5	1 20 mm.
37	Bgbv 82	26·3	7·2	3·25	2·63	1 20 mm.
45	*United Kingdom:* FV 432	15·28	5·251	2·8	1·879	1 7·62 mm. m.g.
43	Spartan	8·172	4·839	2·184	2·25	1 7·62 mm. m.g.
44	Sultan	7·918	4·991	2·184	2·016	1 7·62 mm. m.g.
	FV 434	17·75	5·72	2·844	2·794	
55	*U.S.A.:* M-113A1	11·156	4·863	2·686	2·5	1 12·7 mm. m.g.
55	M-106A1	11·996	4·926	2·863	2·5	1 107 mm. mortar
56	M-577A1	11·513	4·862	2·686	2·68	
57	M-114A1	6·928	4·463	2·33	2·155	1 25 mm. or 1 12·7 mm. m.g 1 7·62 mm. m.g.
57	Lynx	8·5	4·597	2·413	2·171	1 12·7 mm. m.g.
58	LVTP-7	23·665	7·943	3·27	3·12	1 12·7 mm. m.g.
64	*Yugoslavia:* M-980	11·00	6·25	2·85	2·50	1 20 mm., 1 Sagger launcher 2 m.g.

Engine	h.p.	Speed km./hr road	Speed km./hr water	Range km.	Crew	Notes
6 cyl. diesel	215	65	5·8	300	3	Height with Saladin turret.
er 6 cyl. diesel	250	60		350	2+8	Model 4K4F AAG has 20 mm. gun.
6 6 cyl. diesel	300	62	11	450	2+18	Height excludes turret. Data is for OT62B.
AM 8 cyl. petrol	250	65		400	1+12	Height excludes turret.
ano-Suiza 8 cyl. sel	280	65	8	600	2+9	
J 6 cyl. diesel	600	75		520	4+6	
ubishi 8 cyl. diesel	220	45		230	2+8	
ubishi 8 cyl. diesel	220	45		230	5	
ubishi 4 cyl. diesel	300	60			2+10	
el V-6 6 cyl. diesel	280	55	8	300	3+8	
		55	6		3+6	
vo 6 cyl. diesel	270	66	8	300	2+9	
vo 6 cyl. diesel	310	56	8	550	4	Armoured Recovery Vehicle.
s-Royce 6 cyl. lti-fuel	240	52	6	580	2+10	
ar 6 cyl. petrol	195	81	6·5	644	3+4	Height to hull top only 1·718 m.
ar 6 cyl. petrol	195	81	6·5	644	3+3	Samaritan ambulance: crew 2+4. stretcher cases or 6 sitting cases.
s-Royce 6 cyl. lti-fuel	240	52	6	480	4	Height includes crane.
eral Motors 6 cyl. sel	215	68	6	483	2+11	
eral Motors 6 cyl. sel	215	68	6	483	6	
eral Motors 6 cyl. sel		68	6	595	5	
vrolet 8 cyl. petrol	160	58	5·4	480	3-4	
oit Diesel 6 cyl.	215	71	6	523	3	1 25-mm. cannon in Dutch vehicles.
oit Diesel 8 cyl.	400	63	13·5	482	3+25	LVTE-7: crew 6.
ano-Suiza 8 cyl. sel	280	70	8	500	3+6/8	

Ref. No.	Type	Weight tons	Metres				Armament
			Length	Length (inc. gun/ missile)	Width	Height	
	France:						
10	155 mm. GCT	41	6·485	10·4	3·15	2·995	1 155 mm. gun, 1 7·62 m. m.g.
10	155 mm. automouv.	17·4	6·22		2·72	2·1	1 155 mm., 1 m.g.
	Germany:						
16	JgdPzK	27·5	6·238	8·75	2·98	2·085	1 90 mm., 1 7·62 mm. m.g. (co-ax) 1 7·62 mm. m.g. (AA)
16	JgdPzR	23	6·43		2·98	1·98	2 launchers SS-11, 1 7· mm. m.g., 1 7·62 mm. m.g. (AA)
	Japan:						
22	155 mm. SP	24	6·64		2·25	3·18	1 155 mm., 1 12·7 mm. m.g.
21	Type 60 (SS-4)	8	4·3		2·23	1·38	2 106 mm. (recoilless) ranging m.g., 1 12·7 m
	Soviet Union:						
26	ASU-85	14	6·0	8·49	2·8	2·1	1 85 mm., 1 7·62 mm. m (co-ax)
31	Frog 5	15	7·00		3·16	3·08	1 launcher
30	Gainful	15	6·80	7·39	3·18	3·33	3 SA6 launchers
32	Scamp	45		14·40	3·60	4·44	1 Scapegoat (SS-14) launcher
32	Scrooge	50		19·00	3·60	5·00	1 Scrooge (SS-15) launc
	Sweden:						
36	Bkv 1A	53	6·55	11·0	3·37	3·35	1 155 mm.
	United Kingdom:						
47	Abbot	16·5	5·709	5·84	2·641	2·489	1 105 mm., 1 7·62 mm
46	FV 438	16·2	5·105		2·972	2·705	1 Swingfire launcher, 1 7·76 mm. m.g.
43	Striker	8·22	4·759		2·184	2·21	1 Swingfire launcher
	U.S.A.:						
59	M-107	28·17	5·72	11·26	3·15	3·68	1 175 mm.
59	M-110	26·5	5·72	7·47	3·15	2·93	1 203 mm.
60	M-109G	24·5	6·25	6·61	3·58	2·80	1 155 mm., 1 7·62 mm m.g.
61	Vulcan	12	4.86		2.69	2.60	1 20 mm (six barrels)
61	Chaparral	12·6	5·89		2·69	2·64	1 sidewinder launcher
60	Lance	10·7	6·55		2·69	2·72	1 Lance launcher

Engine	h.p.	Speed km./hr road	water	Range km.	Crew	Notes
ano-Suiza 12 cyl. el	700	60		450	4	
AM 8 cyl. petrol	250	65		300	2	
ler–Benz 8 cyl. el	500	70		400	4	
ler–Benz 8 cyl. el	500	70		400	4	Height is to hull top.
ibishi diesel	420	50			6	
atsu 6 cyl. diesel	120	48		130	3	Height guns raised.
l V-6 6 cyl. diesel	240	44		260	4	
l V-6 6 cyl. diesel	240				3	
l V-6 6 cyl. diesel	240	44		260	3	
diesel	690					
diesel	690					
-Royce 6 cyl. el / ng gas turbine	240} 300}	24		230	6	
-Royce 6 cyl. ti-fuel	240	48	5	390	4	
-Royce 6 cyl. ti-fuel	240	52	6·0	480	3	
ar 6 cyl. petrol	195	81	6·5	644	3	
oit Diesel 8 cyl.	405	56		725	5	
oit Diesel 8 cyl.	405	56		725	5	
oit Diesel 8 cyl.	405	56	6·5	390	6	
ral Motors 6 cyl. el	215	68	6		2	
ral Motors 6 cyl. el	215	68			3	
ral Motors 6 cyl. el	215	65			6	

Ref. No.	Type	Weight	Metres			Armament
			Length	Width	Height	
12	*France:* AMX 30 B/L	43	11·5	3·95	4·29	
11	AMX 30 ARV	36	7·20	3·15	2·65	1 7·62 mm. m.g.
17	*Germany:* Leopard B/L	45·3	11·40	4·;0	3·50	
17	Leopard ARV	39·8	7·57	3·25	2·46	
22	*Japan:* Type 67 AVLB	35	7·27	3·5	3·5	
33	*Soviet Union:* T.54 MTU	36	12·00	3·28	2·65	
37	*Sweden:* Brobv 941	28·4	17·00	4·00	3·50	1 m.g.
48	*United Kingdom:* Chieftain AVLB	53·3	13·73	4·16	3·92	
49	Chieftain ARV	53·2	8·25	3·52	2·75	1 7·62 mm. m.g.
50	Combat Engineer Tractor	17·1	7·544	2·896	2·667	
49	Centurion BARV	40·63	8·08	3·40	3·45	
63	*U.S.A.:* M-728 CEV	52	7·88	3·70	3·20	1 165 mm., 1 7·62 mm. m.g. (co 1 12·7 mm. m.g. (AA)
63	M-60 AVLB	55·75	11·048	4·00	4·04	
62	M-88 ARV	50·8	8·25	3·43	2·92	1 12·7 mm. m.g.
62	M-578 ARV	24·47	5·94	3·15	2·92	1 12·7 mm. m.g.

Engine	h.p.	Speed km./hr		Range km.	Crew	Notes
		road	water			
ano-Suiza 12 cyl. sel	700	50			3	Bridge: 22 m. long. Dimensions of vehicle with bridge.
ano-Suiza 12 cyl. sel	700	60			4	
nler–Benz 10 cyl. sel	830	62				Bridge: 22 m. long. Dimensions of vehicle with bridge.
	830	65			4	
ubishi 12 cyl. diesel	600	45		200	3	Bridge: 22 m. long. Dimensions of vehicle with bridge.
el V-54 12 cyl. disel	550	48				Bridge: 12 m.
o-Penta 6 cyl. diesel	310	56	8	550	4	Bridge: 15 m. Dimensions of vehicle with bridge.
		42			3	Bridge: 24·4 m. Dimensions are with bridge.
and 12 cyl. multi-	720	42		500	4	
s-Royce 6 cyl. diesel	320	60	9		2	
s-Royce 12 cyl. rol	650	34			4	
inental 12 cyl. diesel	750	48		500	4	Length inc. jib 9·3 m.
inental 12 cyl. diesel	750	48		500	2	Bridge: 19·2 m. Dimensions of vehicle with bridge.
inental 12 cyl. rol	980	48		360	4	Length excludes dozer blade.
ral Motors 8 cyl. el	425	60		725	3	Length 6·42 m. including crane.